ESSENTIAL SKILLS IN MATHS

Answer Book

BOOK 5

Nelson

Graham Newman and Ron Bull

National Curriculum coverage

Book	1	2	3	4	5
Levels	3–4	4–5	5–6	6–7	7–8

Thomas Nelson and Sons Ltd
Nelson House   Mayfield Road
Walton-on-Thames   Surrey
KT12 5PL   UK

© R. Bull, G. Newman 1997

First published by Thomas Nelson and Sons Ltd 1997

I(T)P   Thomas Nelson is an International Thomson Publishing Company.

I(T)P   is used under licence.

ISBN 0-17-431467-1
NPN 9 8 7 6 5 4 3 2

Printed in China

Contents

NUMBER

ALGEBRA

SHAPE, SPACE AND MEASURES

HANDLING DATA

Number

1 MENTAL ARITHMETIC: MULTIPLICATION AND DIVISION

Exercise 1A

1 3700	**2** 20 400	**3** 19
4 1760	**5** 2.51	**6** 22 800
7 160 000	**8** 1.14	**9** 89.7
10 99 000	**11** 1700	**12** 5500
13 0.4	**14** 26 100	**15** 2.93
16 42	**17** 12 300	**18** 0.809
19 4200	**20** 7.52	**21** 456 000
22 16.4	**23** 9.06	**24** 70
25 237 600	**26** 372 000	**27** 6.12
28 306 400	**29** 8.38	**30** 0.632

Exercise 1B

1 770	**2** 1110	**3** 8400
4 27.8	**5** 8.37	**6** 6900
7 39 200	**8** 57.6	**9** 6.94
10 40 000	**11** 0.291	**12** 52.4
13 31 200	**14** 8.06	**15** 12 250
16 50 000	**17** 0.854	**18** 918 000
19 7.75	**20** 30.7	**21** 132 300
22 4 320 000	**23** 4.47	**24** 7040
25 9.75	**26** 0.795	**27** 62 000
28 0.949	**29** 22.8	**30** 1 120 000

2 USING A CALCULATOR

Exercise 2A

1 1.915	**2** 25.066	**3** 3.097
4 3.585	**5** 0.283	**6** 33.12
7 6.223	**8** 119.905	**9** 163.796
10 117.209	**11** 2.965	**12** 0.113
13 0.770	**14** 0.577	**15** 31.858
16 11.050	**17** 0.183	**18** 0.293
19 0.772	**20** 17.742	**21** 4.947
22 9.293	**23** 1.145	**24** 0.248
25 3.346	**26** 2.463	**27** 2.32
28 18.293	**29** 53.125	**30** 0.076

Exercise 2B

1 7.678	**2** 0.664	**3** 18.089
4 239.908	**5** 49.754	**6** 41.109

7 27.448	**8** 10.871	**9** 2.516
10 30.983	**11** 0.997	**12** 219.171
13 8.355	**14** 8.632	**15** 0.088
16 0.012	**17** 6.359	**18** 11.326
19 20.078	**20** 0.332	**21** 0.479
22 1.295	**23** 279.548	**24** 0.841
25 486.648	**26** 0.042	**27** 11.735
28 3.071	**29** 70.912	**30** 0.074

3 ESTIMATES FOR CALCULATIONS

Exercise 3A

1 36 000	**2** 90	**3** 1000	**4** 20
5 18	**6** 0.175	**7** 1	**8** 15
9 400	**10** 2	**11** $22\frac{1}{2}$	**12** $\frac{4}{5}$
13 90	**14** 400	**15** 100	**16** 120
17 16	**18** 50	**19** $4\frac{1}{2}$	**20** 0.5
21 6.25	**22** 100	**23** 4500	**24** 400
25 18	**26** 1.6	**27** 101.25	**28** 10
29 320	**30** 12.5		

Exercise 3B

1 800	**2** 800	**3** 24 000	**4** 20
5 5	**6** 1600	**7** 4	**8** 10
9 50	**10** $3\frac{1}{2}$	**11** 400	**12** $22\frac{2}{9}$
13 10	**14** 400	**15** 3500	**16** 1000
17 3	**18** 4	**19** 800	**20** 4
21 10	**22** 32	**23** 10 000	**24** 200
25 125	**26** 75	**27** 2000	**28** 50
29 $5\frac{1}{3}$	**30** 8		

4 MEASUREMENT AS AN APPROXIMATION

Exercise 4A

1 (a) 16.5 mm	(b) 17.5 mm
2 (a) 22.5 cl	(b) 23.5 cl
3 (a) 84.5 km	(b) 85.5 km
4 (a) 0.2135 s	(b) 0.2145 s
5 (a) 1.265 cm^2	(b) 1.275 cm^2
6 (a) 4.2735 kg	(b) 4.2745 kg
7 (a) 3.135 m^2	(b) 3.145 m^2

8 (a) 8.905 ml   (b) 8.915 ml
9 (a) 26.15 l (b) 26.25 l
10 (a) 96.5 m.p.h.   (b) 97.5 m.p.h.
11 (a) 15.25 t   (b) 15.35 t
12 (a) 3.265 km^2 (b) 3.275 km^2
13 (a) 0.3205 cm^3 (b) 0.3215 cm^3
14 (a) 50.5 g   (b) 51.5 g
15 (a) 55.5545 m^3 (b) 55.5555 m^3
16 (a) 4.4035 t   (b) 4.4045 t
17 (a) 96.45 m^2 (b) 96.55 m^2
18 (a) 12.4205 m   (b) 12.4215 m
19 (a) 11.5 km/h   (b) 12.5 km/h
20 (a) 78.45 s   (b) 78.55 s
21 (a) 2.745 g   (b) 2.755 g
22 (a) 10.45 cm^3 (b) 10.55 cm^3
23 (a) 33.3325 km   (b) 33.3335 km
24 (a) 2.255 cm   (b) 2.265 cm
25 (a) 27.5445 m^3 (b) 27.5455 m^3
26 (a) 81.5 km   (b) 82.5 km
27 (a) 0.6645 kg   (b) 0.6655 kg
28 (a) 43.05 ml   (b) 43.15 ml
29 (a) 7.4235 s   (b) 7.4245 s
30 (a) 1.200 45 l (b) 1.200 55 l

Exercise 4B

1 (a) 31.5 l (b) 32.5 l
2 (a) 102.5 t   (b) 103.5 t
3 (a) 93.5 km^2 (b) 94.5 km^2
4 (a) 1.025 cl   (b) 1.035 cl
5 (a) 4.4455 t   (b) 4.4465 t
6 (a) 7.2525 cm^3 (b) 7.2535 cm^3
7 (a) 4.185 cm^2 (b) 4.195 cm^2
8 (a) 23.8525 m^3 (b) 23.8535 m^3
9 (a) 4.2765 t   (b) 4.2775 t
10 (a) 1.875 cl   (b) 1.885 cl
11 (a) 5.7065 cm^3 (b) 5.7075 cm^3
12 (a) 20.5 km/h   (b) 21.5 km/h
13 (a) 17.4125 m   (b) 17.4135 m
14 (a) 85.65 s   (b) 85.75 s
15 (a) 3.2585 m^3 (b) 3.2595 m^3
16 (a) 35.65 ml   (b) 35.75 ml
17 (a) 4.3305 m   (b) 4.3315 m
18 (a) 74.5 m.p.h.   (b) 75.5 m.p.h.
19 (a) 3.1245 kg   (b) 3.1255 kg
20 (a) 18.75 g   (b) 18.85 g
21 (a) 7.8635 cm   (b) 7.8645 cm
22 (a) 66.75 s   (b) 66.85 s
23 (a) 52.35 m^2 (b) 52.45 m^2
24 (a) 4.2235 km   (b) 4.2245 km
25 (a) 8.585 l (b) 8.595 l
26 (a) 39.5 km^2 (b) 40.5 km^2
27 (a) 0.515 s   (b) 0.525 s

28 (a) 6.695 cm^2 (b) 6.705 cm^2
29 (a) 2.599 45 l (b) 2.599 55 l
30 (a) 3.435 ml   (b) 3.445 ml

5 EXPRESSING A POSITIVE INTEGER AS A PRODUCT OF PRIMES

Exercise 5A

1 $2 \times 2 \times 5 = 2^2 \times 5$
2 $3 \times 5 \times 5 = 3 \times 5^2$
3 $2 \times 3 \times 7$
4 $2 \times 5 \times 11$
5 $2 \times 2 \times 11 = 2^2 \times 11$
6 $2 \times 7 \times 13$
7 $2 \times 11 \times 19$
8 $2 \times 2 \times 19 = 2^2 \times 19$
9 $3 \times 3 \times 7 = 3^2 \times 7$
10 $2 \times 3 \times 3 = 2 \times 3^2$
11 $5 \times 11 \times 11 = 5 \times 11^2$
12 $2 \times 2 \times 2 \times 2 \times 3 = 2^4 \times 3$
13 $5 \times 5 \times 13 = 5^2 \times 13$
14 $3 \times 11 \times 23$
15 $2 \times 2 \times 2 \times 5 \times 5 \times 5 = 2^3 \times 5^3$
16 $2 \times 3 \times 3 \times 3 = 2 \times 3^3$
17 $2 \times 2 \times 2 \times 7 = 2^3 \times 7$
18 $3 \times 3 \times 11 = 3^2 \times 11$
19 $2 \times 2 \times 7 = 2^2 \times 7$
20 $2 \times 3 \times 5 \times 13$
21 $2 \times 2 \times 29 = 2^2 \times 29$
22 $3 \times 5 \times 23$
23 $2 \times 2 \times 3 \times 3 \times 3 = 2^2 \times 3^3$
24 $2 \times 5 \times 17$
25 $3 \times 3 \times 3 \times 13 = 3^3 \times 13$
26 $3 \times 5 \times 7 \times 13 \times 19$
27 $2 \times 2 \times 23 = 2^2 \times 23$
28 $2 \times 2 \times 7 \times 19 = 2^2 \times 7 \times 19$
29 $17 \times 17 = 17^2$
30 $2 \times 2 \times 2 \times 3 \times 3 \times 5 = 2^3 \times 3^2 \times 5$

Exercise 5B

1 $2 \times 2 \times 7 = 2^2 \times 7$
2 $2 \times 5 \times 7$
3 $2 \times 2 \times 3 \times 7 = 2^2 \times 3 \times 7$
4 $2 \times 3 \times 19$
5 $3 \times 5 \times 13$
6 $2 \times 2 \times 13 = 2^2 \times 13$
7 $2 \times 7 \times 23$
8 $3 \times 3 \times 5 = 3^2 \times 5$
9 $2 \times 2 \times 2 \times 2 \times 3 \times 3 = 2^4 \times 3^2$
10 $2 \times 11 \times 17$
11 $2 \times 3 \times 17$

12 $2 \times 2 \times 23 = 2^2 \times 23$
13 $2 \times 3 \times 11 \times 11 = 2 \times 3 \times 11^2$
14 $5 \times 11 \times 13$
15 $3 \times 3 \times 3 \times 7 = 3^3 \times 7$
16 $5 \times 5 \times 17 = 5^2 \times 17$
17 $2 \times 5 \times 23$
18 $7 \times 7 \times 13 = 7^2 \times 13$
19 $2 \times 2 \times 11 = 2^2 \times 11$
20 $5 \times 5 \times 5 \times 5 = 5^4$
21 $2 \times 7 \times 17$
22 $2 \times 5 \times 11 \times 19$
23 3×5
24 $2 \times 2 \times 2 \times 9 = 2^3 \times 9$
25 $2 \times 3 \times 29$
26 $3 \times 3 \times 31 = 3^2 \times 31$
27 $2 \times 2 \times 37 = 2^2 \times 37$
28 $2 \times 3 \times 3 \times 3 \times 3 = 2 \times 3^4$
29 $2 \times 3 \times 5 \times 7 \times 11 \times 13$
30 $2 \times 2 \times 3 \times 3 \times 3 \times 5 \times 5 = 2^2 \times 3^3 \times 5^2$

6 STANDARD FORM: CONVERTING TO ORDINARY NUMBERS

Exercise 6A

1	1950	**2**	534	**3**	1170
4	227	**5**	32 150	**6**	2720
7	2100	**8**	401	**9**	89 400
10	9400	**11**	8203	**12**	910
13	491 200	**14**	350	**15**	1 913 000
16	987 500	**17**	1 981 000	**18**	149
19	58 124 000	**20**	902 000	**21**	4121
22	311.7	**23**	492 000	**24**	145.9
25	13 970	**26**	3100	**27**	3 821 000
28	2047	**29**	64 900	**30**	6 282 100

Exercise 6B

1	83 700	**2**	1360	**3**	9770
4	809 800	**5**	135	**6**	40 420
7	345	**8**	420.3	**9**	3142
10	13 060	**11**	420	**12**	1017
13	418 900	**14**	1222	**15**	1 801 000
16	87 960 000	**17**	175 900	**18**	139
19	8525	**20**	31 400	**21**	1603
22	130 100	**23**	412.7	**24**	1 432 000
25	1611	**26**	270	**27**	18 720
28	2814	**29**	382.4	**30**	48 150

Exercise 6C

1	0.004 85	**2**	0.087
3	0.241	**4**	0.0472
5	0.004 91	**6**	0.0912
7	0.000 225 5	**8**	0.019 23
9	0.4216	**10**	0.000 024 721
11	0.0947	**12**	0.005 715
13	0.3104	**14**	0.000 584
15	0.000 004 213	**16**	0.2525
17	0.000 061 25	**18**	0.003 128
19	0.1427	**20**	0.000 801 4
21	0.037 68	**22**	0.571
23	0.006 127	**24**	0.041 91
25	0.003 47	**26**	0.000 301 2
27	0.071 18	**28**	0.000 001 792
29	0.008 129	**30**	0.000 021 7

Exercise 6D

1	0.0923	**2**	0.0023
3	0.0763	**4**	0.003 12
5	0.9128	**6**	0.000 419 7
7	0.000 081 99	**8**	0.5573
9	0.000 908	**10**	0.009 147
11	0.032 89	**12**	0.7525
13	0.000 147 2	**14**	0.0729
15	0.009 147	**16**	0.0212
17	0.000 823 2	**18**	0.479
19	0.004 721	**20**	0.8125
21	0.0914	**22**	0.000 673 2
23	0.002 55	**24**	0.000 041 29
25	0.28	**26**	0.000 007 129
27	0.002 176	**28**	0.087
29	0.000 499 1	**30**	0.0892

7 STANDARD FORM: CONVERTING FROM ORDINARY NUMBERS

Exercise 7A

1	2.9×10^4	**2**	4.85×10^3
3	6.0×10^2	**4**	4.3×10^3
5	1.13×10^8	**6**	7.42×10^2
7	9.172×10^3	**8**	7.6×10^5
9	5.6×10^7	**10**	6.28×10^5
11	1.9×10^5	**12**	1.0×10^4
13	2.1×10^7	**14**	4.02×10^3
15	5.83×10^4	**16**	5.78×10^4
17	3.7×10^3	**18**	2.743×10^6
19	4.5×10^4	**20**	6.76×10^5
21	7.29×10^7	**22**	7.07×10^4
23	3.284×10^5	**24**	5.112×10^5
25	7.27×10^8	**26**	2.4×10^4
27	5.734×10^5	**28**	5.1×10^5
29	2.5×10^6	**30**	$2.541 \, 27 \times 10^5$

Exercise 7B

1	3.2×10^4	**2**	5.73×10^5
3	7.0×10^3	**4**	2.7×10^5

5 9.3×10^6

6 1.834×10^4

7 7.0×10^4

8 2.26×10^8

9 9.27×10^4

10 4.66×10^4

11 7.05×10^3

12 5.9×10^7

13 7.21×10^4

14 4.52×10^2

15 1.0×10^5

16 3.3×10^5

17 2.83×10^5

18 2.1403×10^4

19 1.04×10^8

20 2.0945×10^5

21 4.21×10^7

22 2.9001×10^5

23 2.4×10^5

24 9.87×10^6

25 $4.853\,45 \times 10^6$

26 2.7×10^7

27 3.9×10^6

28 1.5×10^5

29 2.75×10^6

30 7.8196×10^4

Exercise 7C

1 9.0×10^{-2}

2 6.0×10^{-3}

3 4.0×10^{-5}

4 1.7×10^{-2}

5 1.01×10^{-2}

6 5.6×10^{-4}

7 9.02×10^{-3}

8 1.0×10^{-1}

9 4.39×10^{-3}

10 6.85×10^{-5}

11 2.7×10^{-4}

12 4.0×10^{-3}

13 2.5×10^{-5}

14 6.2×10^{-3}

15 8.61×10^{-4}

16 3.2×10^{-3}

17 8.2×10^{-4}

18 1.17×10^{-5}

19 9.8×10^{-2}

20 1.662×10^{-3}

21 4.0×10^{-6}

22 8.219×10^{-3}

23 1.001×10^{-3}

24 2.0×10^{-1}

25 7.63×10^{-4}

26 2.7×10^{-5}

27 8.219×10^{-3}

28 7.61×10^{-2}

29 1.01×10^{-5}

30 4.72×10^{-3}

Exercise 7D

1 7.0×10^{-3}

2 2.0×10^{-2}

3 3.0×10^{-4}

4 5.57×10^{-4}

5 1.0001×10^{-3}

6 8.5×10^{-4}

7 8.71×10^{-2}

8 7.2×10^{-4}

9 8.47×10^{-3}

10 1.0×10^{-2}

11 8.4×10^{-4}

12 2.7×10^{-3}

13 2.5×10^{-4}

14 3.3×10^{-2}

15 7.236×10^{-2}

16 3.4×10^{-3}

17 2.42×10^{-4}

18 9.0×10^{-5}

19 8.764×10^{-2}

20 2.42×10^{-5}

21 1.01×10^{-4}

22 7.2×10^{-3}

23 2.0×10^{-4}

24 4.4×10^{-3}

25 7.0×10^{-3}

26 3.47×10^{-5}

27 1.011×10^{-3}

28 2.137×10^{-2}

29 4.97×10^{-4}

30 3.637×10^{-3}

8 CALCULATING WITH STANDARD FORM

Exercise 8A

1 1.38×10^{-3}

2 6.12×10^3

3 8.0×10^6

4 1.0×10^9

5 2.025×10^{11}

6 7.4×10^5

7 2.4×10^6

8 5.12×10^{-10}

9 4.1×10^2

10 3.0×10^5

11 7.48×10^9

12 3.2×10^{-6}

13 1.3×10^2

14 7.0×10^6

15 3.84×10^5

16 3.83×10^{-5}

17 7.5×10^3

18 2.856×10^{20}

19 9.104×10^{-10}

20 4.44×10^{-1}

21 4.664×10^{-14}

22 6.146×10^2

23 7.68×10^{-5}

24 4.731×10^{16} km

25 3.578×10^{-2} mm

26 1.004×10^{-17} g

27 7×10^{-13} s

28 4.458×10^{-21} g

29 500 s

30 1.022×10^{26} kg

Exercise 8B

1 5.184×10^{-9}

2 1.2×10^8

3 3.5×10^{-4}

4 4.0×10^4

5 8.0×10^2

6 8.503×10^{18}

7 5.742×10^{-1}

8 7.614×10^{-7}

9 1.2×10^3

10 5.91×10^7

11 6.0×10^3

12 4.0×10^4

13 6.77×10^{-3}

14 6.48×10^{-3}

15 5.0×10^4

16 5.0×10^{14}

17 6.241×10^{13}

18 7.5×10^{-3}

19 6.774×10^{-4}

20 1.057×10^{11}

21 1.305×10^{-11}

22 1.471×10^6

23 5.26×10^{-5}

24 5.687×10^{26} kg

25 7.779×10^8 km

26 4.555×10^{-24} g

27 7.0×10^{-2} mm

28 3.993×10^{13} km

29 1.25×10^{-13} s

30 4.02×10^{-21} g

REVISION

Exercise A

1 (a) 20.84   (b) 1 570 000   (c) 0.302

(d) 18 630

2 (a) 10.513   (b) 4.703   (c) 138.884

(d) 16.562

3 (a) 800   (b) 10   (c) 25   (d) 5

4 (a) $2 \times 2 \times 2 \times 2 \times 5 \times 9 = 2^4 \times 5 \times 9$

(b) $2 \times 2 \times 2 \times 2 \times 2 \times 3 \times 3 \times 7 = 2^5 \times 3^2 \times 7$

(c) $3 \times 3 \times 3 \times 3 \times 3 \times 5 = 3^5 \times 5$

(d) $2 \times 2 \times 3 \times 5 \times 7 \times 7 = 2^2 \times 3 \times 5 \times 7^2$

5 (a) 521 700   (b) 0.045 96
    (c) 81 040 000   (d) 0.000 002 375
6 (a) 3.0×10^6 (b) 7.9×10^{-4} (c) 7.5×10^8
    (d) 9.0×10^{-6}

Exercise AA

1 £60
2 $800 \div 20 = 40$
3 $500 \div 10 = £50$
4 $5 \times 80 = 400$ kg
5 (a) 8.65×10^5 (b) 3.67×10^9 (c) 3.0×10^8
6 (a) 4.545 m   (b) 4.555 m
7 (a) 82.5 cm   (b) 83.5 cm
8 (a) 84.25 g   (b) 84.35 g
9 (a) 0.0745 s   (b) 0.0755 s
10 9.4×10^{12}
11 2.76×10^{-21}
12 10 000 km/h or 1.0×10^4 km/h
13 1.899×10^{27} kg
14 3.421×10^{-2} mm
15 6×10^{-13} s

9 DIRECT PROPORTION

Exercise 9A

1 32 min
2 300 km
3 £162
4 £450
5 3420 words
6 £287.84
7 465
8 1258 *l*
9 336.6 g
10 16.1 cm
11 17.6 kg
12 224 miles
13 1 h 12 min
14 £13
15 £13.13
16 36p
17 36 seedlings
18 £10.80
19 26.5625 m
20 £3.96

Exercise 9B

1 £68.60
2 £132
3 160 km
4 £8.64
5 £15.60
6 £25.20
7 4.8 cm
8 $37\frac{1}{2}$ min
9 £41.93
10 5.625 kg
11 70p
12 105
13 225 books
14 1785 km
15 2.250 tonnes
16 £20
17 $67\frac{1}{2}$ kg
18 5 h 20 min
19 £8.40
20 £3

10 INVERSE PROPORTION

Exercise 10A

1 $1\frac{1}{2}$ days
2 35
3 2 days
4 8 h 6 min
5 30 weeks
6 12
7 27 cm
8 $6\frac{2}{3}$ weeks
9 50
10 63 m.p.h.
11 12 days
12 16 min
13 80 min
14 9 days
15 20
16 36 days
17 $73\frac{1}{2}$ h
18 4 days
19 3 h
20 36 minutes

Exercise 10B

1 5 h 6 min
2 $5\frac{1}{4}$ h
3 980
4 16 cm
5 30 days
6 $3\frac{1}{3}$ h
7 $66\frac{2}{3}$ h
8 114.8 km
9 232
10 £75
11 $6\frac{2}{3}$ h
12 49
13 12 weeks
14 8 days
15 300
16 25 m
17 8 days
18 £18
19 6 h
20 27 min

11 SIMPLE INTEREST

Exercise 11A

1 £16
2 £64
3 £105
4 £178.50
5 £75
6 £110.25
7 £276
8 £166.50
9 £170.63
10 £281.53
11 £198.45
12 £263.11
13 £358.40
14 £143.50
15 £265.05
16 £18.78
17 £136.50
18 £66.68
19 £208.83
20 £196.66

Exercise 11B

1 £84
2 £90
3 £192
4 £285
5 £156
6 £84.40
7 £41.25
8 £375
9 £269.34
10 £217.80
11 £187
12 £245.44
13 £147
14 £230
15 £18.80
16 £114.45
17 £329.18
18 £61.88
19 £408.72
20 £225.47

Exercise 11C

1 $R = 6\%$
2 $P = £6400$
3 $T = 1\frac{1}{2}$ y
4 $P = £650$
5 $P = £116.67$
6 $R = 9\%$
7 $T = 1$ y
8 $P = £1200$
9 $T = 4\frac{1}{2}$ y
10 $T = 5$ y 8 m
11 $R = 5\%$
12 $P = £2250$
13 $R = 2\frac{1}{2}\%$
14 $P = £740$
15 $R = 5\%$
16 $P = £520$
17 $T = 12$ y
18 $T = 2$ y 2 m
19 $P = £952.38$
20 $R = 4\frac{1}{2}\%$

Exercise 11D

1 $P = £400$
2 $R = 2\frac{1}{2}\%$
3 $T = 6$ y
4 $R = 7\frac{1}{2}\%$
5 $P = £480$
6 $P = £360$
7 $T = 4$ y 3 m
8 $T = 3\frac{1}{2}$ y
9 $R = 4\frac{1}{2}\%$
10 $R = 4\%$
11 $T = 1$ y
12 $R = 6\frac{1}{4}\%$
13 $T = 7\frac{1}{2}$ y
14 $P = £380$
15 $P = £450$
16 $T = 2$ y 2 m
17 $R = 8\%$
18 $R = 4\frac{1}{2}\%$
19 $P = £10\,000$
20 $T = 1$ y 7 m

12 COMPOUND INTEREST

Exercise 12A

1 £25.63
2 £57.96
3 £95.51
4 £46.97
5 £97.39
6 £105.06
7 £157.59
8 £147.51
9 £88.36
10 £24.97
11 £17.25
12 £25.54
13 £125.70
14 £25.44
15 £49.09
16 £29.87
17 £38.21
18 £22.72
19 £131.64
20 £77.43

Exercise 12B

1 £75.35
2 £55.62
3 £63.05
4 £118.62
5 £64.42
6 £94.19
7 £62.59
8 £186.99
9 £48.69
10 £21.92
11 £43.10
12 £1900.83
13 £38.45
14 £51.21
15 £10.31
16 £15.38
17 £49.50
18 £55.23
19 £368.49
20 £60.36

13 INVERSE PERCENTAGE

Exercise 13A

1 £60
2 £160
3 £240
4 £960
5 £87.20
6 100 kg
7 £2400
8 £650
9 £800
10 £260
11 £25
12 £20
13 £12 500
14 375 cm^2
15 £8150
16 £60 000
17 £1.50
18 £3.00
19 12 cm
20 175

Exercise 13B

1 £200
2 £800
3 £64
4 £12 800
5 £1000
6 £1200
7 £30
8 £40
9 £620
10 £4.00
11 250 kg
12 900
13 £18.75
14 40 cm
15 24
16 £65 000
17 £16
18 £180
19 £14 560
20 £62 150

14 GENERAL PROBLEMS

Exercise 14A

1 £14.96
2 (a) £307.50 (b) 2.46p
3 £211.50
4 (a) £245 (b) £220.50
5 8.57%
6 £5.08 per hour
7 £39.00
8 £1586.25
9 1.875 litres
10 £600
11 (a) 2p (b) 2.8%
12 (a) £250 (b) £50
13 9.7%
14 £80.15
15 £105.54
16 £115.15
17 £28.45
18 £54.10
19 £27.80
20 (a) £5905.80 (b) £955.80

Exercise 14B

1 £31.20
2 £41.05
3 £3.96
4 £78.00
5 £183.07
6 £157.50
7 (a) £517.00 (b) £167.00
8 £140.80
9 £124.05
10 5%
11 21 months
12 £123.80
13 $12\frac{1}{2}\%$
14 £93.02
15 £94.71
16 £13.52
17 £186.55
18 (a) £272.88 (b) £47.88
19 £487
20 £31.25

15 ADDITION OF FRACTIONS

Exercise 15A

1. $\frac{1}{3}$ 2. $\frac{9}{20}$ 3. $\frac{11}{15}$

4. $\frac{19}{20}$ 5. $\frac{19}{28}$ 6. $\frac{28}{45}$

7. $1\frac{1}{2}$ 8. $\frac{11}{12}$ 9. $1\frac{19}{36}$

10. $1\frac{5}{12}$ 11. $1\frac{3}{10}$ 12. $1\frac{11}{36}$

13. $5\frac{5}{9}$ 14. $10\frac{9}{14}$ 15. $7\frac{5}{8}$

16. $11\frac{1}{2}$ 17. $6\frac{5}{12}$ 18. $8\frac{11}{20}$

19. $6\frac{1}{3}$ 20. $8\frac{23}{36}$ 21. $9\frac{1}{8}$

22. $8\frac{1}{2}$ 23. $7\frac{19}{24}$ 24. $4\frac{5}{36}$

25. $6\frac{17}{30}$ 26. $8\frac{7}{8}$ litres   27. $6\frac{1}{9}$ hectares

28. $6\frac{1}{4}$ kg   29. $12\frac{1}{2}$ cm   30. $6\frac{1}{4}$ metres

Exercise 15B

1. $\frac{5}{12}$ 2. $\frac{3}{10}$ 3. $\frac{14}{15}$

4. $\frac{11}{12}$ 5. $\frac{37}{56}$ 6. $\frac{24}{35}$

7. $1\frac{1}{2}$ 8. $1\frac{3}{20}$ 9. $1\frac{1}{6}$

10. $1\frac{1}{30}$ 11. $1\frac{1}{10}$ 12. $1\frac{11}{30}$

13. $4\frac{1}{3}$ 14. $5\frac{5}{6}$ 15. $8\frac{1}{4}$

16. $6\frac{17}{20}$ 17. $5\frac{17}{20}$ 18. $8\frac{1}{4}$

19. $8\frac{1}{2}$ 20. $9\frac{7}{10}$ 21. $8\frac{4}{15}$

22. $7\frac{7}{22}$ 23. $5\frac{1}{4}$ 24. $8\frac{11}{14}$

25. $7\frac{1}{8}$ 26. $12\frac{5}{12}$ m   27. $23\frac{1}{3}$ cm

28. $4\frac{1}{8}$ l 29. $\frac{3}{28}$ 30. $3\frac{7}{12}$ kg

16 SUBTRACTION OF FRACTIONS

Exercise 16A

1. $\frac{5}{14}$ 2. $\frac{1}{2}$ 3. $\frac{5}{18}$

4. $\frac{9}{40}$ 5. $\frac{13}{24}$ 6. $\frac{1}{15}$

7. $\frac{7}{20}$ 8. $3\frac{26}{45}$ 9. $3\frac{3}{20}$

10. $7\frac{13}{20}$ 11. $2\frac{13}{36}$ 12. $1\frac{1}{6}$

13. $6\frac{7}{16}$ 14. $2\frac{5}{12}$ 15. $2\frac{9}{20}$

16. $8\frac{17}{40}$ 17. $4\frac{8}{15}$ 18. $2\frac{5}{18}$

19. $3\frac{1}{2}$ 20. $2\frac{7}{9}$ 21. $7\frac{1}{2}$

22. $2\frac{1}{30}$ 23. $\frac{11}{12}$ 24. $\frac{27}{35}$

25. $5\frac{8}{15}$ 26. $1\frac{11}{20}$ kg   27. $1\frac{9}{40}$ hectares

28. $1\frac{23}{40}$ l 29. $1\frac{1}{10}$ feet   30. $2\frac{19}{30}$

Exercise 16B

1. $\frac{1}{4}$ 2. $\frac{1}{2}$ 3. $\frac{3}{8}$

4. $\frac{1}{10}$ 5. $\frac{1}{12}$ 6. $\frac{11}{20}$

7. $\frac{1}{9}$ 8. $4\frac{4}{15}$ 9. $2\frac{5}{24}$

10. $2\frac{7}{48}$ 11. $6\frac{17}{36}$ 12. $2\frac{3}{8}$

13. $4\frac{1}{2}$ 14. $2\frac{11}{15}$ 15. $2\frac{3}{8}$

16. $2\frac{5}{12}$ 17. $1\frac{11}{60}$ 18. $3\frac{13}{24}$

19. $3\frac{1}{4}$ 20. $1\frac{9}{10}$ 21. $\frac{5}{8}$

22. $1\frac{3}{4}$ 23. $\frac{9}{20}$ 24. $1\frac{7}{10}$

25. $\frac{19}{45}$ 26. $5\frac{1}{8}$ l 27. $\frac{1}{6}$

28. $5\frac{5}{8}$ kg   29. $2\frac{7}{8}$ m   30. $7\frac{9}{40}$ m

17 MULTIPLICATION OF FRACTIONS

Exercise 17A

1. 6   2. 10   3. $1\frac{1}{2}$

4. 18   5. $\frac{1}{2}$ 6. $\frac{3}{10}$

7. $\frac{1}{3}$ 8. $\frac{1}{7}$ 9. $\frac{5}{14}$

10. $\frac{1}{12}$ 11. $\frac{3}{10}$ 12. $\frac{1}{4}$

13. $\frac{3}{5}$ 14. $1\frac{7}{8}$ 15. $12\frac{3}{8}$

16. 3   17. $20\frac{2}{9}$ 18. $16\frac{1}{5}$

19. $32\frac{1}{2}$ 20. 9   21. $7\frac{7}{15}$

22. $5\frac{1}{7}$ 23. $44\frac{1}{3}$ 24. 4

25. $10\frac{2}{5}$ 26. $1l$ 27. 1 km

28. $1\frac{19}{20}$ hectares   29. $2\frac{13}{16}$ m   30. $4\frac{3}{8}$ l

Exercise 17B

1. 6   2. 4   3. 24

4. 30   5. $\frac{3}{10}$ 6. $\frac{7}{36}$

7. $\frac{2}{3}$ 8. $\frac{1}{2}$ 9. $\frac{2}{5}$

10. $\frac{1}{6}$ 11. $\frac{4}{7}$ 12. $\frac{2}{3}$

13 $\frac{3}{4}$ **14** $5\frac{5}{8}$ **15** $\frac{15}{16}$

16 $2\frac{1}{5}$ **17** $2\frac{1}{4}$ **18** $7\frac{1}{5}$

19 11 **20** 9 **21** 20

22 $12\frac{4}{7}$ **23** $10\frac{5}{16}$ **24** $3\frac{7}{16}$

25 6 **26** $\frac{5}{9}$ **27** $1\frac{5}{9}$

28 $6\frac{3}{16}$ **29** $\frac{14}{15}$ **30** $4\frac{1}{5}$

18 DIVISION OF FRACTIONS

Exercise 18A

1 $\frac{1}{12}$ **2** $\frac{3}{10}$ **3** $\frac{4}{45}$

4 $\frac{8}{15}$ **5** $\frac{11}{32}$ **6** $2\frac{7}{16}$

7 $\frac{3}{4}$ **8** $1\frac{1}{5}$ **9** $2\frac{5}{8}$

10 $3\frac{1}{4}$ **11** $\frac{7}{8}$ **12** $1\frac{1}{14}$

13 $2\frac{1}{2}$ **14** $1\frac{1}{4}$ **15** $2\frac{1}{2}$

16 $3\frac{5}{6}$ **17** $1\frac{1}{2}$ **18** $\frac{4}{7}$

19 $\frac{1}{2}$ **20** $1\frac{2}{7}$ **21** $\frac{2}{5}$

22 $1\frac{31}{33}$ **23** 1 **24** 2

25 3 **26** 13 m **27** 12 kg

28 $8\frac{7}{10}$ days **29** $6l$ **30** $9\frac{1}{21}$ h

Exercise 18B

1 $\frac{2}{9}$ **2** $\frac{1}{16}$ **3** $\frac{3}{16}$

4 $\frac{13}{16}$ **5** $\frac{11}{15}$ **6** $\frac{26}{35}$

7 $\frac{2}{3}$ **8** $1\frac{1}{8}$ **9** $1\frac{2}{9}$

10 $1\frac{5}{8}$ **11** $\frac{27}{32}$ **12** $\frac{8}{15}$

13 $\frac{3}{4}$ **14** $1\frac{7}{9}$ **15** 2

16 3 **17** $1\frac{1}{5}$ **18** $3\frac{1}{5}$

19 $1\frac{1}{5}$ **20** $2\frac{2}{3}$ **21** $3\frac{2}{3}$

22 2 **23** $2\frac{2}{7}$ **24** $2\frac{1}{4}$

25 $\frac{25}{44}$ **26** 10 **27** 7

28 5 **29** $15\frac{9}{20}$ days **30** 10

REVISION

Exercise B

1 £75

2 $3\frac{1}{3}$ y

3 £500

4 7%

5 £109.26

6 £161.07

7 (a) $\frac{17}{24}$ (b) $6\frac{7}{16}$ (c) $5\frac{9}{10}$

8 (a) $\frac{1}{6}$ (b) $1\frac{1}{24}$ (c) $3\frac{17}{35}$

9 (a) $\frac{8}{15}$ (b) $\frac{2}{3}$ (c) $5\frac{1}{4}$

10 (a) $\frac{4}{35}$ (b) $1\frac{5}{8}$ (c) $5\frac{2}{11}$

Exercise BB

1 420 parts

2 12 boxes

3 20 units

4 8 days

5 $4\frac{1}{2}$ days

6 49 h

7 950 kg

8 £105

9 950

10 52 m

11 £5.28

12 $6\frac{2}{3}$ y

13 £10 000

14 £12.98

15 £3156.62

16 $16\frac{14}{15}$ cm

17 $2\frac{1}{40}$ ton

18 $14\frac{7}{10}$ hectares

19 $6\frac{2}{9}$ h

20 £176

Algebra

19 MAKING PREDICTIONS AND GENERALISING IN NUMBER SERIES

Symbolic answers given are not unique and there are acceptable alternatives in some cases, for example, $n^2 + 2n + 1 = (n + 1)^2$, $n^2 + 3n = n(n + 3)$.

Exercise 19A

1 $2n - 2$; 18, 38
2 $4n + 1$; 61, 81
3 $3n + 3$; 45, 57
4 $2n - 5$; 27, 39
5 $3n - 4$; 32, 56
6 $2n + 3$; 35, 43
7 $5n - 1$; 64, 89
8 $3n + 4$; 58, 70
9 $6n - 1$; 77, 107
10 $4n + 5$; 61, 85
11 $7n - 2$; 82, 124
12 $4n - 4$; 56, 76
13 $n^2 + 1$; 101, 485
14 $3n^2$; 192, 675
15 $n^2 - 2$; 98, 223
16 $n^2 - n$; 90, 132
17 $n^2 + 2n$; 63, 120
18 $n^2 + n - 1$; 109, 239
19 $2n^2 + 2$; 74, 202
20 $n^2 + 3n$; 88, 180
21 $n^2 + n + 2$; 74, 158
22 $n^2 + 4n$; 77, 140
23 $2n^2 - 1$; 71, 199
24 $n^2 + 2n + 1$; 81, 169
25 $2n^2 - n$; 190, 435
26 $3n^2 + 1$; 148, 678
27 $2n^2 + 3n$; 90, 230
28 $3n^2 + 2n$; 161, 456
29 $2n^2 + n + 1$; 137, 466
30 $4n^2 + 2$; 146, 402

Exercise 19B

1 $3n + 1$; 46, 61
2 $2n - 4$; 36, 46
3 $4n - 1$; 47, 71
4 $2n + 4$; 34, 84
5 $3n - 2$; 58, 73
6 $5n + 3$; 53, 78
7 $2n + 6$; 30, 42
8 $3n - 3$; 42, 57
9 $6n - 2$; 40, 58
10 $4n - 3$; 45, 77
11 $5n + 2$; 52, 92
12 $8n + 3$; 83, 123
13 $2n^2$; 128, 288
14 $n^2 + 3$; 228, 403
15 $n^2 + n$; 72, 156
16 $n^2 - 4$; 140, 221
17 $n^2 - 2n$; 80, 195
18 $2n^2 + 4$; 132, 292
19 $n^2 + n - 3$; 107, 237
20 $2n^2 + n$; 136, 300
21 $3n^2 + n$; 154, 310
22 $n^2 + n + 4$; 114, 244
23 $2n^2 + 2n$; 144, 220
24 $3n^2 - 2$; 145, 298
25 $2n^2 + n - 1$; 135, 299
26 $n^2 - 3n$; 70, 180
27 $3n^2 - 2n$; 176, 408
28 $2n^2 - 2n$; 112, 264
29 $3n^2 - n$; 290, 574
30 $5n^2 - 1$; 312, 719

20 MULTIPLICATION OF TERMS

Exercise 20A

1 $4x^2$
2 $12c^2$
3 $10a^2b^2$
4 $8y^3$
5 x^5
6 $12y^3$
7 $3b^3$
8 y^6
9 $16x^2$
10 $9a^2$
11 $30t^2$
12 $4a^2b^2$
13 $4x^4$
14 $12y^5$
15 $6c^7$
16 $4y^9$
17 $21qr$
18 $27y^3$
19 $20f^7$
20 $32pq$
21 $6y^9$
22 $20d^2$
23 $9acd$
24 a^2b^2
25 $2e^2fg$
26 x^6
27 $3st^2$
28 $6g^2h^2$

Exercise 20B

1 $12x^2$
2 $9c^2$
3 $3c^2d^2$
4 $6a^3$
5 $6x^2$
6 a^5
7 $6x^3$
8 x^8
9 $16b^2$
10 $12w^2$
11 $6x^8$
12 $21g^8$
13 $4a^2b^2$
14 $6c^2d^2$
15 $15y^7$
16 $24x^6$
17 $12xy$
18 $8x^6$
19 $18abc$
20 $9x^2$
21 $24abc$
22 $6xy^2$
23 $30ab$
24 ab^2c
25 y^{12}
26 $6cd^2$
27 $4d^2e^2$
28 $27d^6$

21 DIVISION OF TERMS

Exercise 21A

1 t^3
2 $2d$
3 1
4 $3x$
5 3
6 x
7 $\dfrac{d}{e}$
8 $\dfrac{5b}{c}$
9 4
10 $3d^3$
11 $\dfrac{y}{4}$
12 $\dfrac{1}{g}$
13 $\dfrac{1}{t^2}$
14 $2x$
15 $\dfrac{p}{2r}$
16 $3y$
17 $\dfrac{x}{y}$
18 $\dfrac{m}{2}$
19 q^2
20 $5xy^2$
21 $2b^3$
22 $\dfrac{1}{y^3}$
23 $\dfrac{2y}{3x}$
24 $2m$
25 $\dfrac{a}{b}$
26 $\dfrac{x}{2}$
27 $\dfrac{q}{3p}$
28 $\dfrac{x}{y}$
29 $\dfrac{3q}{2w}$
30 $\dfrac{3tu}{2s}$

Exercise 21B

1 f^4
2 $\dfrac{x}{w}$
3 $4g$
4 2

5 $5y$ **6** $12g^5$ **7** w^2 **8** 1

9 $\dfrac{4e}{f}$ **10** $2b$ **11** km **12** $\dfrac{1}{j}$

13 $3a$ **14** $2f$ **15** $\dfrac{a}{bc}$ **16** $\dfrac{4a}{5}$

17 $\dfrac{x}{3}$ **18** $\dfrac{4a}{d}$ **19** $\dfrac{4x}{y}$ **20** $2n$

21 $\dfrac{n}{3}$ **22** 3 **23** $\dfrac{5}{a^2}$ **24** $\dfrac{q}{2}$

25 $\dfrac{10x^3}{y^3}$ **26** n **27** $\dfrac{1}{x}$ **28** $\dfrac{p}{q}$

29 $\dfrac{s^2}{w}$ **30** $2b$

22 BRACKETS

Exercise 22A

1 $5x + 20$ **2** $3x + 4$
3 $m - 4n$ **4** $16x^2 - 40x$
5 $x + 43$ **6** $5d - 2$
7 $6x^3 + 8x$ **8** $4cd + 2ce + 6cf$
9 $11x + 69$ **10** $2xy + 2wx$
11 $9x^4 + 6x^3 - 21x^2$ **12** $17g - 10$
13 $6 - 5x$ **14** $1 + 18t$
15 $p + 18q$ **16** $2a + 20$
17 $4x - 7y$ **18** $10a^2b + 20ab^2$
19 $6x + 19$ **20** $ab - 11a$
21 $4 - 16x$ **22** $3xy + 16x$
23 $9b - 31$ **24** $6x^3y + 4xy^2$
25 $2ab + 6ac$ **26** $3x + 20$
27 $10x^2y^2 + 15x^3$ **28** $12x$
29 $9x + 2y$ **30** $2x + 8$

Exercise 22B

1 $7x + 23$ **2** $4x + 5y$
3 $13k - m$ **4** $7x + 22$
5 $5x^2 + 30x$ **6** $2e + 3$
7 $8x^3 + 4x$ **8** $6x - 26$
9 $13 - 8x$ **10** $24x^3 - 48x^2 + 8x$
11 $16k - 17m$ **12** $2 - 2x$
13 $4u^2 - 5$ **14** $12p$
15 $2d + 6e$ **16** $17de - 2ce$
17 $10 - 12g$ **18** $6p^3q + 8pq^2$
19 $7x - 2$ **20** $cd + 8ce$
21 $7 - 9c$ **22** $x^2 + 2x^3$
23 $9p + 13$ **24** $14ax - 20bx$
25 $19 - 2x$ **26** $3x^2 + 3x^4$
27 $13c + 2d$ **28** $12x - 48y$
29 $5 - 18x + 15y$ **30** $46x + 10y$

23 EXPANSIONS

Exercise 23A

1 $x^2 + 10x + 21$ **2** $x^2 + 5x - 24$
3 $x^2 - 2x - 8$ **4** $x^2 - 9x + 18$
5 $x^2 + 8x + 16$ **6** $x^2 - 12x + 36$
7 $3x^2 - 13x - 30$ **8** $24x^2 + 38x + 8$
9 $8x^2 - 14x + 3$ **10** $4x^2 + 20x + 25$
11 $16x^2 + 2x - 3$ **12** $x^2 + 4x - 12$
13 $3x^2 - 10x - 8$ **14** $36x^2 - 25$
15 $4x^2 - 16x - 9$ **16** $x^2 + 8x + 15$
17 $10x^2 - 11x - 6$ **18** $16x^2 - 1$
19 $4x^2 - 25$ **20** $9x^2 - 6x + 1$
21 $81x^2 - 25$ **22** $30 + 7x - 2x^2$
23 $2a^2 - ab - 6b^2$ **24** $4a^2 - b^2$
25 $20y^2 - 11yz - 4z^2$ **26** $25t^2 - 4$
27 $10x^2 + 9xy + 2y^2$ **28** $15x^2 + xy - 2y^2$
29 $6x^2 + 23xy + 15y^2$ **30** $2x^2 + 5xy + 3y^2$

Exercise 23B

1 $x^2 + 7x + 10$ **2** $x^2 + 4x - 21$
3 $x^2 + 7x - 18$ **4** $x^2 - 15x + 56$
5 $x^2 - 4x + 4$ **6** $x^2 + 10x + 25$
7 $8x^2 + 14x + 5$ **8** $10x^2 + 7x - 12$
9 $6x^2 + 7x - 20$ **10** $6x^2 - 13x - 28$
11 $6x^2 - 29x + 28$ **12** $10x^2 + 19x + 6$
13 $4x^2 - 20x + 25$ **14** $9x^2 - 4$
15 $15x^2 - 14x - 8$ **16** $12x^2 + 17x - 5$
17 $16x^2 - 81$ **18** $9x^2 + 6x - 35$
19 $24x^2 + 23x + 5$ **20** $9x^2 + 24x + 16$
21 $12x^2 - 19x - 21$ **22** $64x^2 - 9$
23 $4x^2 + 12x + 9$ **24** $9x^2 - 12xy - 5y^2$
25 $18p^2 - 27pq - 5q^2$ **26** $4x^2 - 4x + 1$
27 $4x^2 + 7xy + 3y^2$ **28** $10x^2 + 21x - 10$
29 $16x^2 - 8xy - 3y^2$ **30** $21x^2 + 34xy + 8y^2$

24 FACTORISING

Exercise 24A

1 $10(10x - y)$ **2** $3u(4 + 5v)$
3 $a(3 + 4b)$ **4** $2(3p - q)$
5 $x(y - 5)$ **6** $n(m - 4)$
7 $x(5y + 7)$ **8** $a(3b - 4c + 5d)$
9 $5z(y + 2)$ **10** $cd(c - d)$
11 $y(3 - 2y^2)$ **12** $5(s^3 + 4)$
13 $7d(2 + 5d)$ **14** $ap(2 + p^2)$
15 $2b(3a + 4c - 2d)$ **16** $5pq(p + 2q)$
17 $a^3bc(a - b)$ **18** $4uv(3u + 4)$

19 $2x(4x + 5)$
20 $3y(3y - 1)$
21 $y(2x + y + 5)$
22 $x(x^2 + 7x + 4)$
23 $3x(2y - 3x)$
24 $5x(1 + 2x)$
25 $2xy(2x - 5y)$
26 $4ab(2 + ab)$
27 $3mn(1 - 2mn)$
28 $5y(y^2 + 2y - 4)$
29 $2x(x^2 - 4x + 1)$
30 $6d^3(d - 1)$

Exercise 24B

1 $2(a + 2b)$
2 $4t(2g + 3h)$
3 $5b(a + 2c)$
4 $3x(y + 2)$
5 $r(pq + st)$
6 $4x(y - 2)$
7 $x(2y - 3z)$
8 $t(u + 5t)$
9 $2z(2y + 3)$
10 $12d^2(3d - 1)$
11 $5c(c - 5d)$
12 $a(2b^2 - 6b + 1)$
13 $d(1 - 6d)$
14 $ax(x + a)$
15 $c(5ab - bd + 2de)$
16 $xyz(x + y + z)$
17 $7a(b^2 - 3a)$
18 $2\pi rh(r + 1)$
19 $a(a - 6b^2)$
20 $3x(x^2 + 5x + 1)$
21 $3x(3x - 4)$
22 $2p^2(4p + 3)$
23 $2x(1 - 4y + 6x)$
24 $x(x^2 + xy + y^2)$
25 $g(13h^2 - 1)$
26 $6x(3x - 2y)$
27 $pq(6 - 5pq)$
28 $2x(x^2 - 3x + 4)$
29 $xy(x^2y^2 - xy + 1)$
30 $4xy(2y - 1)$

25 SUBSTITUTION

Exercise 25A

1 3
2 $6\frac{2}{3}$
3 $\frac{8}{9}$
4 $13\frac{4}{9}$

5 4
6 $90\frac{4}{9}$
7 $27\frac{4}{9}$
8 8

9 −18
10 3

11 (a) 3.575 (b) 8
12 (a) 62.8 (b) 3.5
13 (a) 5 (b) 2.5
14 (a) 21.2 (b) 20.2
15 (a) 5.5873 (b) 7
16 (a) 4400 (b) 4.5
17 (a) 9.4015 (b) 3
18 (a) 6.909 (b) 7
19 (a) 2.5 (b) 29
20 (a) 21 (b) 7
21 (a) 4 (b) 5
22 (a) 18.84 (b) 1.33
23 (a) 2 (b) 3
24 (a) 32 (b) 6
25 (a) 169.39 (b) 10
26 (a) 1.25 (b) 4.5
27 (a) 8.14 (b) 9
28 (a) 18.75 (b) 5
29 (a) 60 (b) 3
30 (a) 14 (b) 5

Exercise 25B

1 $10\frac{1}{2}$
2 $1\frac{7}{18}$
3 $7\frac{1}{2}$
4 66

5 $9\frac{5}{6}$
6 1
7 18 225
8 $405\frac{25}{36}$

9 $96\frac{25}{36}$
10 $21\frac{3}{5}$

11 (a) $1\frac{2}{3}$ (b) 7
12 (a) 160 (b) 5
13 (a) 2464 (b) 7
14 (a) 6.75 (b) 4
15 (a) −3 (b) 12
16 (a) 28 (b) 7

17 (a) 26.6 (b) −5
18 (a) 8 (b) 8
19 (a) 2.6159 (b) 100
20 (a) 875 (b) 5
21 (a) 594 (b) 35
22 (a) −50 (b) 41
23 (a) 80 (b) 2
24 (a) −7.2 (b) 3
25 (a) 32 (b) 2
26 (a) 2.5 (b) 4
27 (a) 4 (b) 3
28 (a) 4 (b) 5
29 (a) −7.5 (b) 2
30 (a) 4.713 (b) 5

26 CHANGING THE SUBJECT OF A FORMULA (1)

Exercise 26A

1 $x = \dfrac{b}{3}$
2 $x = 5d$

3 $x = 4 - f$
4 $x = g + h$

5 $x = \dfrac{y + 9}{6}$
6 $x = \dfrac{5y + 2}{6}$

7 $x = \dfrac{y - 9}{5}$
8 $x = \dfrac{y + 4}{3}$

9 $x = \dfrac{3p - q}{2}$
10 $x = \dfrac{y}{a} - 3$

11 $x = \dfrac{2}{a} + b$
12 $x = 2(a + 3)$

13 $x = \dfrac{4(d - 1)}{3}$
14 $x = ac - b$

15 $x = qt + p$
16 $r = p - q$

17 $a = \dfrac{c + d}{b}$
18 $k = 3 + pq$

19 $t = r - s$
20 $q = \dfrac{1 - pr}{p}$

21 $m = n - l$
22 $Q = 3P - R$

23 $t = \dfrac{s - v}{5}$
24 $s = \dfrac{v}{t}$

25 $a = 2s - b - c$
26 $s = \dfrac{u^2 - v^2}{2a}$

27 $b = \dfrac{A}{l}$
28 $t = \dfrac{S - u}{3}$

29 $b = \dfrac{A - ah}{h}$
30 $b = \dfrac{1 - 2c}{2}$

Exercise 26B

1 $x = \dfrac{y}{4}$
2 $x = 2a$

3 $x = c + e$
4 $x = 5 - m$

5 $x = \dfrac{y + 8}{2}$
6 $x = \dfrac{7y - 2}{8}$

7 $x = \dfrac{y - 3}{2}$
8 $x = \dfrac{y + 1}{4}$

9 $x = \dfrac{2q + p}{3}$
10 $x = \dfrac{y + 4a}{a}$

11 $x = \dfrac{c - xd}{a}$

12 $x = 4a - 8$

13 $x = \dfrac{4c + 8}{3}$

14 $x = 4y + 5$

15 $x = 6 + y$

16 $d = ab - c$

17 $s = r + t$

18 $z = \dfrac{y}{x}$

19 $p = \dfrac{h - 4}{q}$

20 $y = \dfrac{xz + 3}{x}$

21 $Q = \dfrac{P}{R}$

22 $R = \dfrac{100I}{PT}$

23 $q = 6 - p^2$

24 $r = \dfrac{c}{2\pi}$

25 $t = \dfrac{u - v}{g}$

26 $u = v - at$

27 $p = \dfrac{3q + 5}{3}$

28 $s = \dfrac{v^2 - u^2}{2a}$

29 $h = \dfrac{2A}{a + b}$

30 $c = 2a - b$

27 CHANGING THE SUBJECT OF A FORMULA (2)

Exercise 27A

1 $x = \dfrac{c}{a - b}$

2 $x = \dfrac{u}{m + 2}$

3 $x = \dfrac{d - q}{p - q}$

4 $x = \dfrac{py}{q + 5}$

5 $x = \dfrac{c + e}{a - d}$

6 $x = \dfrac{r}{p + q}$

7 $x = \dfrac{ay}{a - b}$

8 $x = \sqrt{b - 4}$

9 $x = \sqrt{a + b}$

10 $x = \sqrt{b^2 - a^2}$

11 $x = \sqrt{4y}$

12 $x = 2 + y^2$

13 $x = pq^2$

14 $x = 2d^2$

15 $x = 20y^2 + 4$

16 $p = \dfrac{r}{q + s}$

17 $b = \dfrac{ac}{a - c}$

18 $p = \sqrt{\dfrac{q}{4}}$

19 $a = \dfrac{c}{b - d}$

20 $g = \dfrac{4d^2}{3}$

21 $a = \dfrac{bc}{b - c}$

22 $c = \dfrac{a^2}{b^2}$

23 $p = \dfrac{q}{q + r}$

24 $x = b^2 - a$

25 $p = \sqrt{6 - q}$

26 $p = -\dfrac{qr}{q + r}$

27 $l = \dfrac{gT^2}{4\pi^2}$

28 $r = \dfrac{p + q}{p - q}$

29 $T = \dfrac{f^2 m}{n^2}$

30 $r = \sqrt{\dfrac{3V}{\pi h}}$

Exercise 27B

1 $x = \dfrac{r}{p + q}$

2 $x = \dfrac{u}{t + 3}$

3 $x = \dfrac{2}{y - z}$

4 $x = \dfrac{c - b}{a - b}$

5 $x = \dfrac{r + s}{p - q}$

6 $x = \dfrac{f}{d - 1}$

7 $x = \dfrac{pq}{p + q}$

8 $x = \sqrt{y + 2}$

9 $x = \sqrt{b - a}$

10 $x = \sqrt{c^2 + d^2}$

11 $x = \sqrt{3y}$

12 $x = b^2 - a$

13 $x = m + n^2$

14 $x = 3y^2$

15 $x = 18y^2 - 1$

16 $a = \dfrac{b}{c - 1}$

17 $p = \sqrt{r^2 - q^2}$

18 $a = \dfrac{d}{b + c}$

19 $q = \dfrac{pr - p}{r + 1}$

20 $c = \dfrac{a^2}{b}$

21 $p = \dfrac{a^2}{4}$

22 $m = \sqrt{p - n}$

23 $a = \sqrt{c - b}$

24 $p = \dfrac{qn}{2q + n}$

25 $c = \dfrac{8b^2}{7}$

26 $q = \dfrac{4p}{a^2}$

27 $a = \dfrac{c - b}{x - y}$

28 $a = c^2 - b$

29 $r = \sqrt{\dfrac{5I}{2m}}$

30 $\sqrt{\dfrac{A + 3r^2}{3}}$

REVISION

Exercise C

1 $4n + 5$; 65, 85

2 $2n^2 - 1$; 199, 449

3 $n^2 + n + 4$; 114, 244

4 $3n^2 + n$; 690, 1220

5 (a) $6a^2$ (b) $4ab$ (c) $4a^2 + a$
    (d) $4xy + 2cd$ (e) x^8 (f) $8c^3$
    (g) $27b^6$ (h) $8y^6$ (i) p^3

    (j) $3a$ (k) $\dfrac{1}{c}$ (l) 4

6 (a) $x + 14$ (b) $2x^3 + 6x$ (c) $22 - 5x$
    (d) $2x + 6y$ (e) $x^2 - 5x + 6$ (f) $2x^2 - 5x - 3$
    (g) $4x^2 - 12x + 9$ (h) $10x^2 + 13xy - 3y^2$

7 (a) $x = \dfrac{bc}{a}$ (b) $x = b - cd$

(c) $x = \dfrac{c + 2a}{a}$ or $\dfrac{c}{a} + 2$

(d) $x = \dfrac{2A}{h} - y$ or $\dfrac{2A - hy}{h}$

(e) $x = \dfrac{c}{a + b}$ (f) $x = \dfrac{a}{b^2}$

Exercise 27

1 $2n + 2$; 18, 28, 38
2 n^2; 100, 225, 400
3 $\frac{1}{2}n(n + 1)$; 55, 120, 210
4 $2n^2 - n$; 190, 435, 780
5 (a) 9.0 (b) 8.8 (c) 0.25
6 (a) 2464 (b) 1.75
7 (a) $-20°C$ (b) $41°F$
8 (a) $x^2 - 8$ (b) $x(x^2 - 8)$

28 SOLVING EQUATIONS

Exercise 28A

1 5	**2** 3	**3** $2\frac{1}{2}$	**4** $5\frac{1}{2}$	**5** $1\frac{1}{4}$
6 3	**7** $1\frac{2}{5}$	**8** $3\frac{2}{3}$	**9** 4	**10** $4\frac{1}{2}$
11 1	**12** $2\frac{1}{2}$	**13** $5\frac{1}{4}$	**14** 6	**15** $1\frac{1}{2}$
16 $8\frac{1}{2}$	**17** $\frac{3}{4}$	**18** 6	**19** $1\frac{1}{2}$	**20** $2\frac{1}{2}$
21 4	**22** 1	**23** 2	**24** 8	**25** 1
26 $7\frac{1}{3}$	**27** $5\frac{1}{2}$	**28** 1	**29** $6\frac{1}{2}$	**30** $2\frac{1}{2}$

Exercise 28B

1 3	**2** $3\frac{1}{2}$	**3** 3	**4** 5	**5** 3
6 7	**7** $\frac{2}{3}$	**8** $4\frac{1}{2}$	**9** $4\frac{1}{2}$	**10** 1
11 $5\frac{1}{2}$	**12** 2	**13** $2\frac{1}{2}$	**14** 3	**15** $4\frac{1}{2}$
16 $9\frac{1}{3}$	**17** $2\frac{1}{2}$	**18** 3	**19** $6\frac{1}{2}$	**20** 3
21 2	**22** 3	**23** 5	**24** 5	**25** 1
26 3	**27** $3\frac{1}{2}$	**28** 2	**29** $8\frac{1}{2}$	**30** $2\frac{1}{2}$

Exercise 28C

1 2	**2** 6	**3** 40	**4** $6\frac{2}{3}$	**5** 5
6 7	**7** 4	**8** 2	**9** 10	**10** 7
11 $3\frac{1}{2}$	**12** 6	**13** 1	**14** $-1\frac{1}{2}$	**15** 4
16 -3	**17** 3	**18** 2	**19** $-\frac{2}{5}$	**20** 2
21 6	**22** 8	**23** -1	**24** $3\frac{1}{2}$	**25** 2
26 1	**27** -3	**28** $1\frac{1}{2}$	**29** 9	**30** 3

Exercise 28D

1 12	**2** 5	**3** 10	**4** 4	**5** 8
6 14	**7** 1	**8** 10	**9** -2	**10** $-2\frac{1}{2}$

11 9	**12** 1	**13** $-6\frac{2}{3}$	**14** -1	**15** 5
16 60	**17** 3	**18** 20	**19** -3	**20** -2
21 -2	**22** 3	**23** -1	**24** 4	**25** $\frac{3}{5}$
26 2	**27** 8	**28** 0	**29** -4	**30** $13\frac{1}{2}$

29 QUADRATIC EQUATIONS: SOLUTION BY TRIAL AND IMPROVEMENT

Exercise 29A

1 2.73, -0.73	**2** 3.79, -0.79
3 3.83, -1.83	**4** 1.37, -4.37
5 1.59	**6** 3.04
7 5.16, -1.16	**8** 2.71
9 5.73	**10** 1.41, 0.59
11 1.92	**12** 1.78, -0.28
13 0.66, -1.18	**14** 3.47
15 0.88, -1.13	**16** -0.22, -2.28
17 4.93	**18** 0.55, -1.22
19 1.74	**20** 1.19, -1.69

Exercise 29B

1 3.65, -1.65	**2** 0.79, -3.79
3 2.19, -3.19	**4** 2.39
5 4.70, -1.70	**6** 2.15
7 2.82	**8** 1.37, -0.37
9 -0.27, -3.73	**10** 3.56
11 0.77, -0.43	**12** 2, -1
13 2.20	**14** 1.44, -0.69
15 3.75	**16** -0.38, -2.62
17 -0.38, -2.62	**18** 3.33
19 0.54, -1.87	**20** 1.88

30 SIMULTANEOUS EQUATIONS: SOLUTION BY ALGEBRAIC METHODS

Exercise 30A

1 $x = 6, y = 2$	**2** $x = 9, y = 5$
3 $x = 0, y = 3$	**4** $x = 9, y = 2$
5 $x = 1, y = 2$	**6** $x = 1, y = 2$
7 $x = 2, y = 1$	**8** $x = 2, y = 3$
9 $x = 2, y = 1$	**10** $x = 2\frac{1}{2}, y = -\frac{1}{2}$
11 $x = 1, y = \frac{1}{2}$	**12** $x = 2, y = 1$
13 $x = 2, y = 3$	**14** $x = -1, y = 4$
15 $x = 4, y = 2$	**16** $x = 1, y = 2$
17 $x = 1, y = 4$	**18** $x = 3, y = 1$
19 $x = 3, y = 2$	**20** $x = \frac{1}{2}, y = 0$
21 $x = 4, y = 1$	**22** $x = 2, y = 8$
23 $x = 4, y = 5$	**24** $x = 4, y = 5$
25 $x = 9, y = -6$	**26** $x = 10, y = 5$
27 $x = 2, y = -2$	**28** $x = 5, y = -1$
29 $x = 1, y = 1$	**30** $x = 6, y = -2$

Exercise 30B

1 $x = 8, y = 3$
2 $x = 3, y = 0$
3 $x = 10, y = -4$
4 $x = 7, y = 1$
5 $x = 3, y = -1$
6 $x = 2, y = 1$
7 $x = \frac{1}{2}, y = \frac{1}{2}$
8 $x = 4, y = -3$
9 $x = 2, y = 8$
10 $x = 4, y = -3$
11 $x = 9, y = 1$
12 $x = 1, y = 2$
13 $x = 12, y = 5$
14 $x = 4, y = -2$
15 $x = 2, y = 1$
16 $x = 3, y = 1$
17 $x = 4, y = 6$
18 $x = 5, y = 1$
19 $x = 8, y = 3$
20 $x = 5, y = 3$
21 $x = 4, y = 3$
22 $x = 1, y = 3$
23 $x = 1, y = 2$
24 $x = 3, y = 7$
25 $x = 2, y = 1$
26 $x = 9, y = 1$
27 $x = 1, y = -2$
28 $x = 2, y = 2$
29 $x = -7, y = 3$
30 $x = 2, y = -3$

Exercise 30C

1 6, 19
2 25, 14
3 36, 30
4 (a) 12p   (b) 18p
5 (a) 38 g (b) 25 g
6 64p, 44p
7 £6, £2
8 (a) 94 g (b) 58 g
9 (a) 60p (b) 70p
10 (a) 30 min (b) 20 min
11 (a) 90p (b) 60p
12 11 m, 8 m
13 60 y, 5 y
14 (a) £400 (b) £200
15 45 y, 15 y

Exercise 30D

1 2, 7
2 18, 9
3 (a) 40p (b) 20p
4 7 y, 3 y
5 (a) £12 (b) £16
6 (a) 20p (b) 22p
7 (a) 5 g (b) 8 g
8 (a) £18 (b) £12
9 (a) £60 (b) £25
10 25 y, 5 y
11 £1232
12 (a) 300 g (b) 250 g
13 24 y, 3 y
14 (a) 4 m (b) 1 m
15 (a) £5 (b) £18

31 FINDING THE EQUATION OF A STRAIGHT-LINE GRAPH

Exercise 31A

1 $y = x + 1$
2 $y = 3x - 2$
3 $y = 2x + 4$
4 $y = 4x$
5 $y = -x + 3$
6 $y = 3x + 1$
7 $y = -3x - 1$
8 $y = -2x + 3$
9 $y = -x$
10 $y = -3x + 4$
11 $y = \frac{1}{2}x + 3$
12 $y = -2x - 1$
13 $y = \frac{1}{2}x$
14 $y = -\frac{1}{2}x - 1$
15 $y = 4x - 3$
16 $y = -\frac{1}{2}x - 4$
17 $y = \frac{1}{4}x + 1$
18 $y = \frac{1}{4}x - 3$

19 $y = 4x + 1$
20 $y = -\frac{1}{4}x + 2$
21 $y = \frac{1}{2}x + 1\frac{1}{2}$
22 $y = -\frac{1}{2}x + 1$
23 $y = \frac{1}{4}x + 3\frac{1}{2}$
24 $y = -\frac{1}{2}x + 3\frac{1}{2}$
25 $y = \frac{1}{2}x + 3\frac{1}{2}$

Exercise 31B

1 $y = 2x + 3$
2 $y = x - 4$
3 $y = 3x - 3$
4 $y = -x + 1$
5 $y = -2x + 2$
6 $y = 3x$
7 $y = -2x - 4$
8 $y = -3x + 1$
9 $y = 3x + 4$
10 $y = -2x$
11 $y = -3x + 3$
12 $y = -3x - 2$
13 $y = \frac{1}{2}x - 1$
14 $y = -\frac{1}{2}x - 3$
15 $y = -\frac{1}{4}x$
16 $y = 2x + 1\frac{1}{2}$
17 $y = -\frac{1}{2}x + 1$
18 $y = 4x - 2$
19 $y = -\frac{1}{4}x + 3$
20 $y = 4x + 3$
21 $y = -\frac{1}{2}x + 1\frac{1}{2}$
22 $y = -\frac{1}{4}x + 3\frac{1}{2}$
23 $y = -\frac{1}{2}x + 2\frac{1}{2}$
24 $y = -\frac{1}{4}x + 1\frac{1}{2}$
25 $y = -\frac{1}{2}x - 1\frac{1}{2}$

32 DRAWING A STRAIGHT-LINE GRAPH FROM AN EQUATION

Exercise 32A

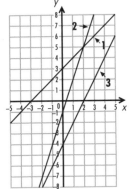

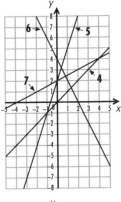

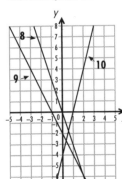

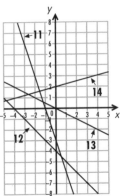

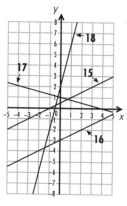

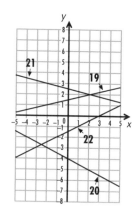

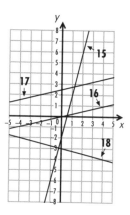

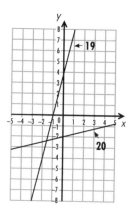

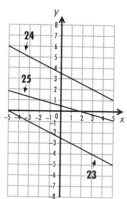

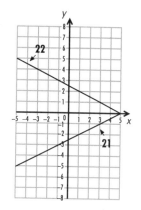

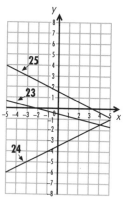

Exercise 32B

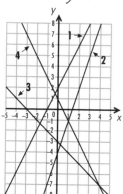

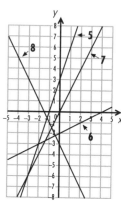

33 SIMULTANEOUS EQUATIONS: SOLUTION BY GRAPHICAL METHODS

Exercise 33A

1 $x = 2$, $y = 2$ **2** $x = 1$, $y = 3$

3 $x = 0$, $y = 1$ **4** $x = 3$, $y = 1$

5 $x = -2$, $y = 0$ **6** $x = -4$, $y = 5$

7 $x = 2$, $y = 2$ **8** $x = 1$, $y = -3$

9 $x = 0$, $y = 1$ **10** $x = -2$, $y = 4$

11

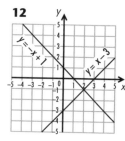

$x = 4$, $y = 3$

12

$x = 2$, $y = -1$

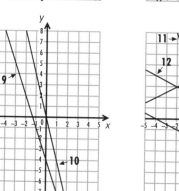

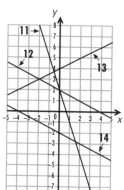

13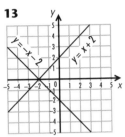
$y = -x - 2$ $y = x + 2$

$x = -2,\ y = 0$

14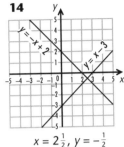
$y = -x + 2$ $y = x - 3$

$x = 2\frac{1}{2},\ y = -\frac{1}{2}$

15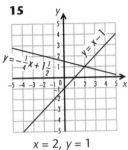
$y = -\frac{1}{4}x + 1\frac{1}{2}$ $y = x - 1$

$x = 2,\ y = 1$

16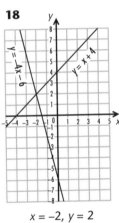
$y = -\frac{1}{4}x + 1\frac{1}{2}$ $y = 2x - 3$

$x = 2,\ y = 1$

17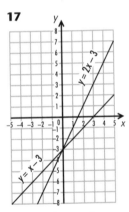
$y = 2x - 3$ $y = x - 3$

$x = 0,\ y = -3$

18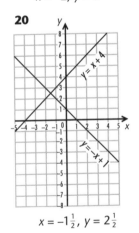
$y = -4x - 6$ $y = x + 4$

$x = -2,\ y = 2$

19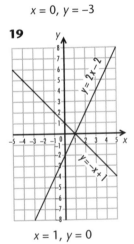
$y = 2x - 2$ $y = -x + 1$

$x = 1,\ y = 0$

20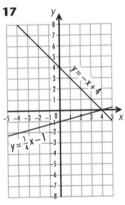
$y = x + 4$ $y = -x + 1$

$x = -1\frac{1}{2},\ y = 2\frac{1}{2}$

Exercise 33B
1 $x = 2,\ y = 2$ **2** $x = -1,\ y = -1$
3 $x = 4,\ y = 3$ **4** $x = -2,\ y = 4$

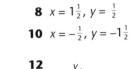
5 $x = 2,\ y = -1$ **6** $x = 3,\ y = 1$
7 $x = 0,\ y = -2$ **8** $x = 1\frac{1}{2},\ y = \frac{1}{2}$
9 $x = 1,\ y = 3$ **10** $x = -\frac{1}{2},\ y = -1\frac{1}{2}$

11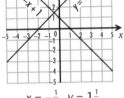
$y = -x + 1$ $y = x + 2$

$x = -\frac{1}{2},\ y = 1\frac{1}{2}$

12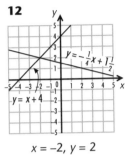
$y = -\frac{1}{4}x + 1\frac{1}{2}$
$y = x + 4$

$x = -2,\ y = 2$

13
$y = -x + 4$ $y = x - 3$

$x = 3\frac{1}{2},\ y = \frac{1}{2}$

14
$y = -\frac{1}{4}x + 1\frac{1}{2}$ $y = -4x - 6$

$x = -2,\ y = 2$

15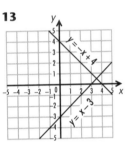
$y = -x - 2$ $y = x - 3$

$x = \frac{1}{2},\ y = -2\frac{1}{2}$

16
$y = -x + 2$ $y = x + 2$

$x = 0,\ y = 2$

17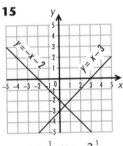
$y = -x + 4$ $y = \frac{1}{4}x - 1$

$x = 4,\ y = 0$

18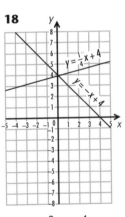
$y = \frac{1}{4}x + 4$ $y = -x + 4$

$x = 0,\ y = 4$

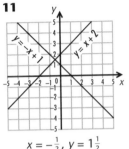
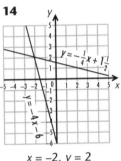
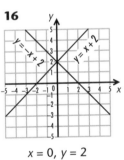

19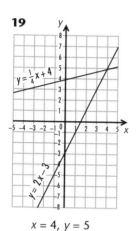

20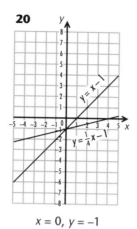

$x = 4, y = 5$ $x = 0, y = -1$

34 INTERPRETING TRAVEL GRAPHS

Exercise 34A

1 (a) 40 m.p.h.   (b) 0930   (c) $1\frac{1}{2}$ h
    (d) 25 miles

2 (a) 22.5 miles   (b) 2 h   (c) 9 m.p.h.

3 (a) 1430   (b) 80 km   (c) 80 km/h
    (d) 30 km

4 (a) 18 and 26 min
    (b) The diver is at the same depth.
    (c) 45 feet
    (d) The diver started the ascent to the surface.

5 (a) The salesman stopped.   (b) 3 h 36 min
    (c) 92 m.p.h.   (d) 460 miles

6 (a) After $\frac{1}{2}$ h   (b) 25 miles   (c) $\frac{1}{2}$ h
    (d) $6\frac{2}{3}$ m.p.h.

7 (a) 20 s   (b) The first 10 seconds
    (c) 300 m   (d) 4 and 59 m

8 (a) The girl returned home.   (b) 1230–1330
    (c) 6 km   (d) 1.5 km/h

Exercise 34B

1 (a) $3\frac{1}{3}$ m.p.h.   (b) 1200   (c) 6 h   (d) 1330

2 (a) 2 metres per minute   (b) 25 min   (c) 36 m

3 (a) 10 and 25 s   (b) 10 ft/s   (c) 25 s
    (d) 43 ft

4 (a) 30 m   (b) 1500   (c) 1 h
    (d) 1330 and 1530

5 (a) 1 h   (b) 30 km/h   (c) 53 km   (d) 42 min

6 (a) 10 min   (b) 15 min   (c) 54 ft

7 (a) 2 h   (b) 80 miles   (c) $32\frac{1}{2}$ miles
    (d) 15 m.p.h.

8 (a) 2 h   (b) 5 km/h   (c) 7 km
    (d) 1345 and 1548

35 DRAWING QUADRATIC GRAPHS

Exercise 35A

1

x	0	1	2	3	4	5
x^2	0	1	4	9	16	25
$-5x$	0	-5	-10	-15	-20	-25
7	7	7	7	7	7	7
y	7	3	1	1	3	7

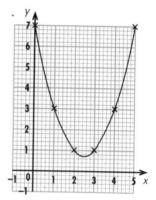

(a) 0.75   (b) 1.75   (c) 0.49, 4.51

2

x	1	2	3	4	5	6	7
x^2	1	4	9	16	25	36	49
$-8x$	-8	-16	-24	-32	-40	-48	-56
12	12	12	12	12	12	12	12
y	5	0	-3	-4	-3	0	5

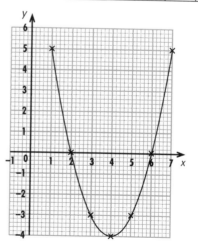

(a) -4 (b) -2.04 (c) 1.76, 6.24

3

x	0	1	2	3	4	5
x^2	0	1	4	9	16	25
$-4x$	0	−4	−8	−12	−16	−20
4	4	4	4	4	4	4
y	4	1	0	1	4	9

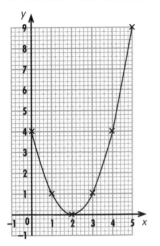

(a) 6.25   (b) 0.39, 3.61

4

x	−1	0	1	2	3	4
x^2	1	0	1	4	9	16
$-3x$	3	0	−3	−6	−9	−12
y	4	0	−2	−2	0	4

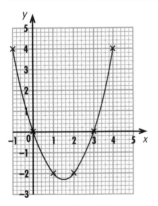

(a) −2.25   (b) 1.75   (c) 0.38, 2.62

5

x	−1	0	1	2	3	4	5
x^2	1	0	1	4	9	16	25
$-3x$	3	0	−3	−6	−9	−12	−15
−1	−1	−1	−1	−1	−1	−1	−1
y	3	−1	−3	−3	−1	3	9

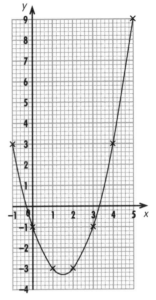

(a) −3.25   (b) 5.16   (c) −0.79, 3.79

6

x	0	1	2	3	4	5
2	2	2	2	2	2	2
$4x$	0	4	8	12	16	20
$-x^2$	0	−1	−4	−9	−16	−25
y	2	5	6	5	2	−3

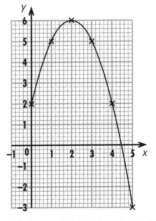

(a) 6   (b) 0.24   (c) 3.73, 0.27

7

x	0	1	2	3	4	5	6
x^2	0	1	4	9	16	25	36
$-6x$	0	−6	−12	−18	−24	−30	−36
8	8	8	8	8	8	8	8
y	8	3	0	−1	0	3	8

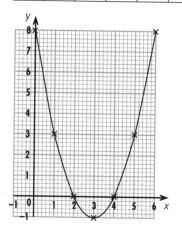

(a) 5.25   (b) 1.33, 4.67

9

x	0	1	2	3	4	5	6
$6x$	0	6	12	18	24	30	36
$-x^2$	0	−1	−4	−9	−16	−25	−36
y	0	5	8	9	8	5	0

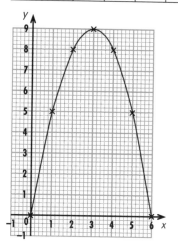

(a) 6.75   (b) 5.45, 0.55

8

x	−1	0	1	2	3	4	5
x^2	1	0	1	4	9	16	25
$-4x$	4	0	−4	−8	−12	−16	−20
3	3	3	3	3	3	3	3
y	8	3	0	−1	0	3	8

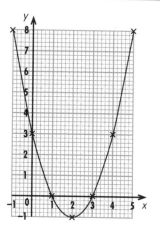

(a) 1.25   (b) −0.83, 4.83

10

x	−3	−2	−1	0	1	2	3
$2x^2$	18	8	2	0	2	8	18
3	3	3	3	3	3	3	3
y	21	11	5	3	5	11	21

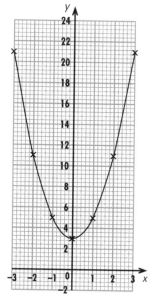

(a) 6.92   (b) −1.87, 1.87

11

x	−1	0	1	2	3	4	5
x^2	1	0	1	4	9	16	25
$-4x$	4	0	−4	−8	−12	−16	−20
y	5	0	−3	−4	−3	0	5

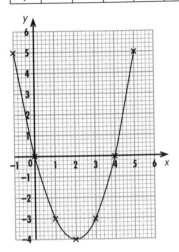

(a) 1.76   (b) −0.83, 4.83

12

x	−2	−1	0	1	2	3	4
8	8	8	8	8	8	8	8
$2x$	−4	−2	0	2	4	6	8
$-x^2$	−4	−1	0	−1	−4	−9	−16
y	0	5	8	9	8	5	0

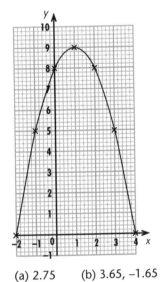

(a) 2.75   (b) 3.65, −1.65

13

x	0	1	2	3	4	5	6
x^2	0	1	4	9	16	25	36
$-7x$	0	−7	−14	−21	−28	−35	−42
10	10	10	10	10	10	10	10
y	10	4	0	−2	−2	0	4

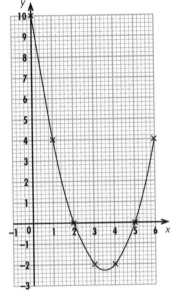

(a) −2.25
(b) −1.25
(c) 1.21, 5.79

14

x	−1	0	1	2	3	4
$4x^2$	4	0	4	16	36	64
$-12x$	12	0	−12	−24	−36	−48
9	9	9	9	9	9	9
y	25	9	1	1	9	25

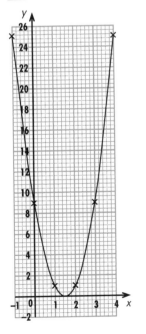

(a) 0
(b) 4
(c) −0.23, 3.23

15

x	−2	−1	0	1	2	3
4	4	4	4	4	4	4
$3x$	−6	−3	0	3	6	9
$-2x^2$	−8	−2	0	−2	−8	−18
y	−10	−1	4	5	2	−5

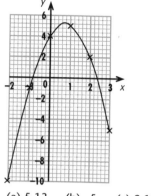

(a) 5.13   (b) −5   (c) 2.19, −0.69

16

x	−3	−2	−1	0	1	2
$2x^2$	18	8	2	0	2	8
$3x$	−9	−6	−3	0	3	6
−4	−4	−4	−4	−4	−4	−4
y	5	−2	−5	−4	1	10

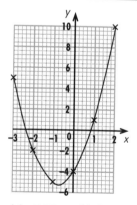

(a) −5.13   (b) 5   (c) −1.90, 0.40

Exercise 35B

1

x	0	1	2	3	4	5	6
x^2	0	1	4	9	16	25	36
$-6x$	0	−6	−12	−18	−24	−30	−36
9	9	9	9	9	9	9	9
y	9	4	1	0	1	4	9

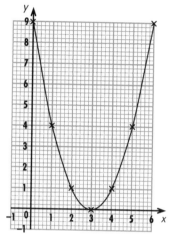

(a) 2.25   (b) 0.76, 5.24

2

x	1	2	3	4	5	6
x^2	1	4	9	16	25	36
$-8x$	−8	−16	−24	−32	−40	−48
15	15	15	15	15	15	15
y	8	3	0	−1	0	3

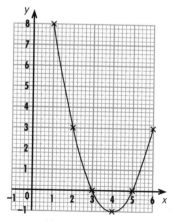

(a) 3.84   (b) 2.59, 5.41

3

x	−3	−2	−1	0	1	2
x^2	9	4	1	0	1	4
$2x$	−6	−4	−2	0	2	4
y	3	0	−1	0	3	8

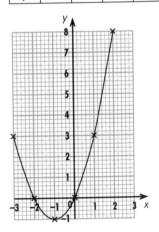

(a) 4.76　　(b) −1.71, −0.29

4

x	1	2	3	4	5	6	7
x^2	1	4	9	16	25	36	49
$-10x$	−10	−20	−30	−40	−50	−60	−70
$+25$	25	25	25	25	25	25	25
y	16	9	4	1	0	1	4

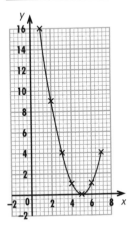

(a) 7.84　　(b) 3.8, 6.4

5

x	0	1	2	3	4	5	6
x^2	0	1	4	9	16	25	36
$-7x$	0	−7	−14	−21	−28	−35	−42
10	10	10	10	10	10	10	10
y	10	4	0	−2	−2	0	4

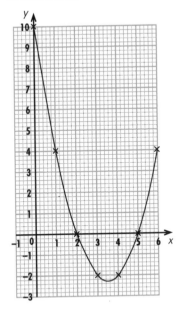

(a) −2.25
(b) 6.75
(c) 1.44, 5.56

6

x	−1	0	1	2	3	4	5
x^2	1	0	1	4	9	16	25
$-3x$	3	0	−3	−6	−9	−12	−15
-4	−4	−4	−4	−4	−4	−4	−4
y	0	−4	−6	−6	−4	0	6

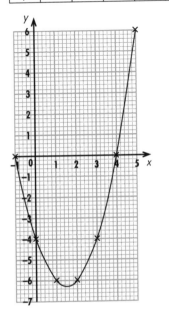

(a) −6.25
(b) 2.16
(c) 0.38, 2.62

7

x	-2	-1	0	1	2	3	4
x^2	4	1	0	1	4	9	16
$-2x$	4	2	0	-2	-4	-6	-8
-8	-8	-8	-8	-8	-8	-8	-8
y	0	-5	-8	-9	-8	-5	0

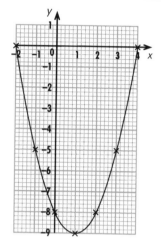

(a) -2.75   (b) -0.41, 2.41

8

x	-2	-1	0	1	2	3	4
x^2	4	1	0	1	4	9	16
$-2x$	4	2	0	-2	-4	-6	-8
3	3	3	3	3	3	3	3
y	11	6	3	2	3	6	11

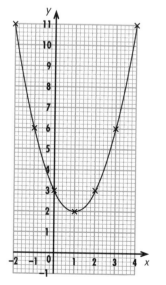

(a) 2.25   (b) -1.45, 3.45

9

x	0	1	2	3	4	5	6
3	3	3	3	3	3	3	3
$6x$	0	6	12	18	24	30	36
$-x^2$	0	-1	-4	-9	-16	-25	-36
y	3	8	11	12	11	8	3

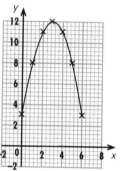

(a) 9.75   (b) 5.24, 0.76

10

x	-1	0	1	2	3	4	5
$4x$	-4	0	4	8	12	16	20
$-x^2$	-1	0	-1	-4	-9	-16	-25
y	-5	0	3	4	3	0	-5

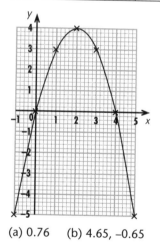

(a) 0.76   (b) 4.65, -0.65

11

x	0	1	2	3	4	5	6
x^2	0	1	4	9	16	25	36
$-7x$	0	-7	-14	-21	-28	-35	-42
7	7	7	7	7	7	7	7
y	7	1	-3	-5	-5	-3	1

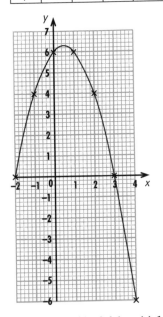

(a) -5.25   (b) -1.64   (c) 1.70, 5.30

12

x	-2	-1	0	1	2	3	4
6	6	6	6	6	6	6	6
x	-2	-1	0	1	2	3	4
$-x^2$	-4	-1	0	-1	-4	-9	-16
y	0	4	6	6	4	0	-6

(a) 6.25   (b) -2.16   (c) 1.62, -0.62

13

x	-2	-1	0	1	2	3	4
5	5	5	5	5	5	5	5
$3x$	-6	-3	0	3	6	9	12
$-x^2$	-4	-1	0	-1	-4	-9	-16
y	-5	1	5	7	7	5	1

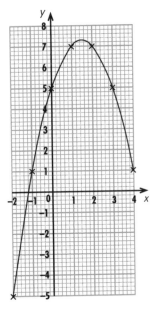

(a) 7.25   (b) -1.75   (c) 2.62, 0.38

14

x	-2	-1	0	1	2	3
$3x^2$	12	3	0	3	12	27
$-3x$	6	3	0	-3	-6	-9
-2	-2	-2	-2	-2	-2	-2
y	16	4	-2	-2	4	16

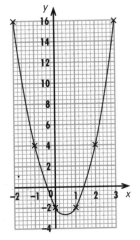

(a) -2.75   (b) 2.32   (c) -1.21, 2.21

15

x	-3	-2	-1	0	1	2	3
$2x^2$	18	8	2	0	2	8	18
-5	-5	-5	-5	-5	-5	-5	-5
y	13	3	-3	-5	-3	3	13

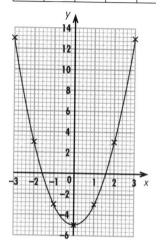

(a) 7.5 (b) −0.71, 0.71

16

x	0	1	2	3	4	5
$2x^2$	0	2	8	18	32	50
$-9x$	0	-9	-18	-27	-36	-45
4	4	4	4	4	4	4
y	4	-3	-6	-5	0	9

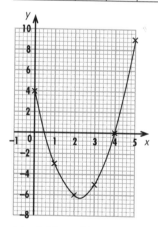

(a) −6.13 (b) 4 (c) 0.30, 4.14

36 QUADRATIC EQUATIONS: SOLUTION BY GRAPHICAL METHODS

Exercise 36A

1 (a) 1.38, 3.62 (b) 0.70, 4.30
2 (a) 2, 6 (b) 2.27, 5.73
3 (a) 2 (b) 0.59, 3.41
4 (a) 0, 3 (b) −0.56, 3.56

5 (a) −0.30, 3.30 (b) 0.38, 2.62
6 (a) 2, 4 (b) 0.55, 5.45
7 (a) 4.45, −0.45 (b) 3.41, 0.59
8 (a) 1, 3 (b) 0.27, 3.73
9 (a) 0, 6 (b) 4.73, 1.27
10 (a) −0.71, 0.71 (b) −2.74, 2.74
11 (a) 0, 4 (b) 0.59, 3.41
12 (a) 4, −2 (b) 2.73, −0.73
13 (a) 2, 5 (b) 1.70, 5.30
14 (a) 1.5 (b) 0.28, 2.72
15 (a) 2.35, −0.85 (b) 2.64, −1.14
16 (a) −2.35, 0.85 (b) −2.64, 1.14

Exercise 36B

1 (a) 3, 3 (b) 1.27, 4.73
2 (a) 3, 5 (b) 2.27, 5.73
3 (a) 0, 2 (b) −2.73, 0.73
4 (a) 5 (b) 3.27, 6.73
5 (a) 2, 5 (b) 2.38, 4.62
6 (a) −1, 4 (b) −0.56, 3.56
7 (a) −2, 4 (b) −1.45, 3.45
8 (a) −1.83, 3.83 (b) −0.73, 2.73
9 (a) 5.65, 0.35 (b) 4.41, 1.59
10 (a) 0, 2 (b) 3.41, 0.59
11 (a) 1.21, 5.79 (b) 0.81, 6.19
12 (a) 3, −2 (b) 3.79, −0.79
13 (a) 3, −2 (b) 2.56, −1.56
14 (a) −0.46, 1.46 (b) −1.48, 2.48
15 (a) −1.58, 1.58 (b) −1.22, 1.22
16 (a) 0.5, 4 (b) 1.22, 3.28

37 DRAWING CUBIC AND RECIPROCAL GRAPHS

Exercise 37A

1

x	-4	-3	-2	-1	1	2	3	4
y	-0.25	-0.33	-0.5	-1	1	0.5	0.33	0.25

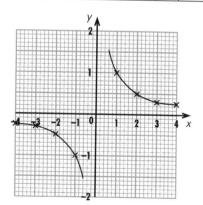

2

x	−4	−3	−2	−1	0	1	2	3	4
x^3	−64	−27	−8	−1	0	1	8	27	64
$9x$	36	27	18	9	0	−9	−18	−27	−36
y	−28	0	10	8	0	−8	−10	0	28

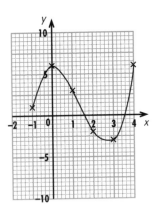

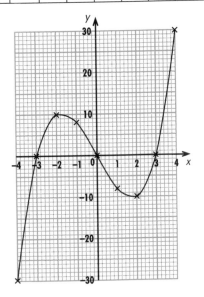

5

x	−4	−3	−2	1	1	2	3	4
y	−1	−1.33	−2	−4	4	2	1.33	1

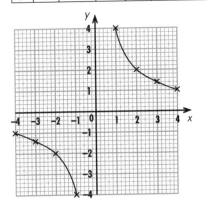

3

x	−3	−2	−1	0	1	2	3
x^3	−27	−8	−1	0	1	8	27
$-9x$	27	18	9	0	−9	−18	−27
2	2	2	2	2	2	2	2
y	2	12	10	2	−6	−8	2

6

x	−3	−2	−1	0	1	2	3
x^3	−27	−8	−1	0	1	8	27
$-x^2$	−9	−4	−1	0	−1	−4	−9
$-6x$	18	12	6	0	−6	−12	−18
y	−18	0	4	0	−6	−8	0

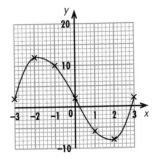

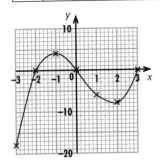

4

x	−1	0	1	2	3	4
x^3	−1	0	1	8	27	64
$-4x^2$	−4	0	−4	−16	−36	−64
6	6	6	6	6	6	6
y	1	6	3	−2	−3	6

7

x	−2	−1	0	1	2	3	4
x^3	−8	−1	0	1	8	27	64
$-2x^2$	−8	−2	0	−2	−8	−18	−32
−10	−10	−10	−10	−10	−10	−10	−10
y	−28	−13	−10	−11	−10	−1	22

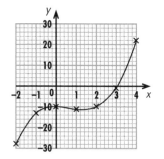

8

x	−1	0	1	2	3	4
x^3	−1	0	1	8	27	64
$-3x^2$	−3	0	−3	−12	−27	−48
y	−4	0	−2	−4	0	16

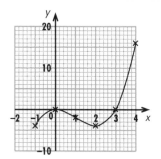

9

x	−2	−1	−0.5	0	1	2	3
x^3	−8	−1	−0.125	0	1	8	27
$-x^2$	−4	−1	−0.25	0	−1	−4	−9
$-2x$	4	2	1.0	0	−2	−4	−6
y	−8	0	0.625	0	−2	0	12

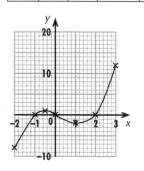

10

x	−4	−3	−2	−1	1	2	3	4
y	−1.75	−2.33	−3.5	−7	7	3.5	2.33	1.75

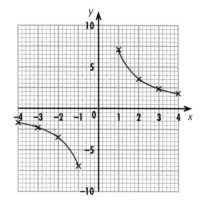

11

x	−3	−2	−1	0	1	2	3
$9x$	−27	−18	−9	0	9	18	27
$-x^2$	−9	−4	−1	0	−1	−4	−9
$-x^3$	27	8	1	0	−1	−8	−27
y	−9	−14	−9	0	7	6	−9

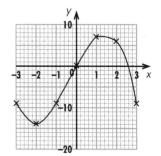

12

x	−1	0	1	2	3	4
x	−1	0	1	2	3	4
$4x^2$	4	0	4	16	36	64
$-x^3$	1	0	−1	−8	−27	−64
y	4	0	4	10	12	4

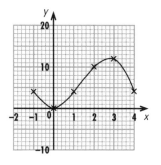

Exercise 37B

1

x	−3	−2	−1	0	1	2	3
x^3	−27	−8	−1	0	1	8	27
$-4x$	12	8	4	0	−4	−8	−12
y	−15	0	3	0	−3	0	15

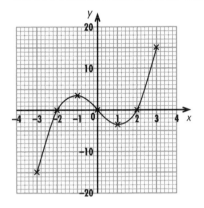

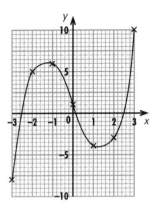

2

x	−4	−3	−2	−1	1	2	3	4
y	−0.5	−0.66	−1	−2	2	1	0.66	0.5

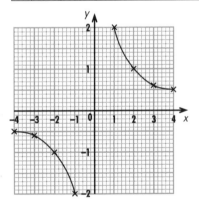

4

x	−2	−1	0	1	2	3
x^3	−8	−1	0	1	8	27
$-4x$	8	4	0	−4	−8	−12
-2	−2	−2	−2	−2	−2	−2
y	−2	1	−2	−5	−2	13

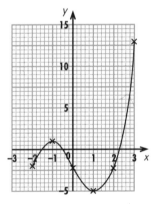

3

x	−3	−2	−1	0	1	2	3
x^3	−27	−8	−1	0	1	8	27
$-6x$	18	12	6	0	−6	−12	−18
1	1	1	1	1	1	1	1
y	−8	5	6	1	−4	−3	10

5

x	−3	−2	−1	0	1	2
x^3	−27	−8	−1	0	1	8
$2x^2$	18	8	2	0	2	8
y	−9	0	1	0	3	16

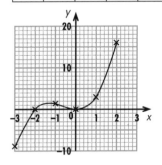

6

x	−4	−3	−2	−1	1	2	3	4
y	−1.25	−1.66	−2.5	−5	5	2.5	1.66	1.25

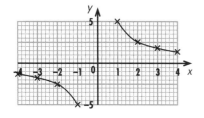

9

x	−3	−2	−1	0	1	2	3	4
x^3	−27	−8	−1	0	1	8	27	64
$-2x^2$	−18	−8	−2	0	−2	−8	−18	−32
$-5x$	15	10	5	0	−5	−10	−18	−20
y	−30	−6	2	0	−6	−10	−6	12

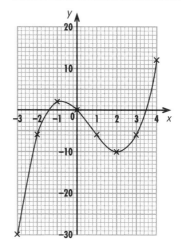

7

x	−2	−1	0	1	2	3	4
$3x^2$	12	3	0	3	12	27	48
$-x^3$	8	1	0	−1	−8	−27	−64
y	20	4	0	2	4	0	−16

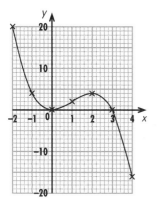

10

x	−4	−3	−2	−1	1	2	3	4
y	−2	−2.66	−4	−8	8	4	2.66	2

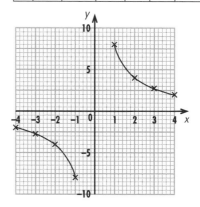

8

x	−2	−1	−0.5	0	0.5	1	2
x^3	−8	−1	−0.125	0	0.125	1	8
$-x$	2	1	0.5	0	−0.5	−1	−2
−2	−2	−2	−2	−2	−2	−2	−2
y	8	−2	−1.625	−2	−2.375	−2	4

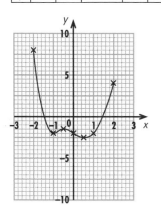

11

x	−2	−1	0	1	2	3
x^3	−8	−1	0	1	4	9
$-4x^2$	−16	−4	0	−4	−8	−12
$3x$	−6	−3	0	3	6	9
y	−30	−8	0	0	2	6

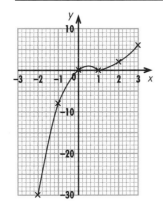

12

x	−2	−1	0	1	2	3	4
$4x$	−8	−4	0	4	8	12	16
$4x^2$	16	4	0	4	16	36	64
$-x^3$	8	1	0	−1	−8	−27	−64
y	16	1	0	7	16	21	16

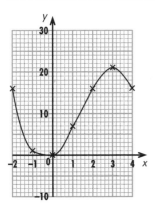

38 RECOGNISING TYPES OF GRAPH FROM EQUATIONS

Exercise 38A

1 F	**2** K	**3** T	**4** L	**5** N
6 M	**7** Q	**8** B	**9** S	**10** E
11 R	**12** A	**13** H	**14** G	**15** I
16 O	**17** J	**18** D	**19** C	**20** P

Exercise 38B

1 H	**2** I	**3** Q	**4** O	**5** S
6 M	**7** L	**8** B	**9** D	**10** A

11 F	**12** P	**13** N	**14** C	**15** E
16 T	**17** R	**18** K	**19** J	**20** G

39 INEQUALITIES

Exercise 39A

1 $x < 2$	**2** $x > -8$	**3** $x > 5$
4 $x \leq -1$	**5** $x \geq -4$	**6** $x < 1$
7 $x > 1$	**8** $x \leq 0$	**9** $-8 \leq x < 0$
10 $-6 < x < -2$	**11** $0 < x \leq 4$	**12** $1 < x \leq 3$
13 $4 \leq x < 9$	**14** $-7 \leq x \leq 0$	**15** $-4 < x \leq -1$

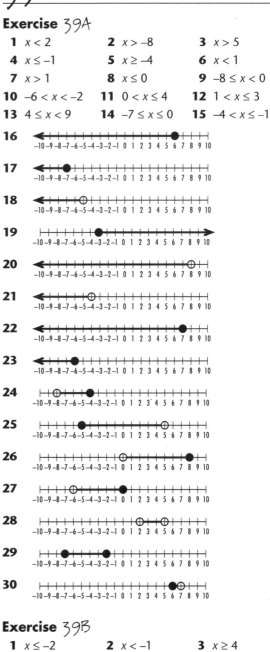

16
17
18
19
20
21
22
23
24
25
26
27
28
29
30

Exercise 39B

1 $x \leq -2$	**2** $x < -1$	**3** $x \geq 4$
4 $x > -6$	**5** $x < -7$	**6** $x \leq -8$
7 $x \leq 5$	**8** $x > -3$	**9** $5 < x < 8$
10 $1 \leq x \leq 7$	**11** $-4 \leq x < 1$	**12** $7 < x \leq 8$
13 $-8 < x < 2$	**14** $6 < x < 8$	**15** $0 \leq x \leq 9$

16

17

18

19

20

21

22

23

24

25

26

27

28

29

30

Exercise 39C

1 −2, −1	**2** −3, −2, −1
3 6	**4** −7, −6, −5, −4
5 3, 4	**6** −3, −2, −1, 0, 1
7 −5, −4, −3, −2, −1, 0	
8 −7, −6, −5, −4, −3, −2, −1, 0	
9 4, 6	**10** 8
11 8, 10	**12** 6
13 None	**14** −4, −2
15 −4	**16** 10
17 5	**18** 5
19 −7, −5, −3	**20** 5
21 3, 5, 7	**22** 5, 7
23 −3, −1	**24** 3

Exercise 39D

1 4, 5, 6	**2** −4, −3, −2, −1
3 −3, −2, −1, 0, 1, 2	**4** 7, 8, 9
5 0, 1, 2, 3, 4	**6** −7, −6, −5, −4, −3
7 3	**8** 6, 7, 8, 9

9 4, 6	**10** 2, 4, 6
11 −6, −4	**12** 2, 4, 6
13 −6, −4, −2, 2, 4, 6	**14** 2, 4, 6, 8
15 8	**16** 2, 4, 6, 8
17 5, 7	**18** −7, −5, −3, −1, 1, 3
19 −5	**20** 3, 5, 7
21 1, 3	**22** 1, 3, 5, 7
23 7	**24** −5, −3, −1

40 INEQUALITIES AND REGIONS

Exercise 40A

1 $x < -1$	**2** $x \geq -1$
3 $y < -2$	**4** $y \geq 3$
5 $x \leq 3$	**6** $y > -3$
7 $x > 1$	**8** $y \leq 2$
9 $x \leq 4$	**10** $x > 0, y > 4$
11 $x \geq -4, y > 5$	**12** $x \geq 1, y \geq -3$
13 $x \leq 1, y > -1$	**14** $x > -2, y \geq -2$
15 $x > 4, y > 3$	

16 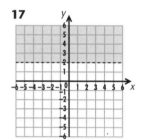 **17**

18 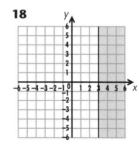 **19**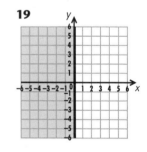

20 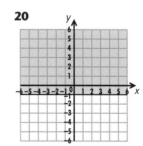 **21**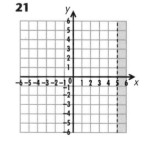

22

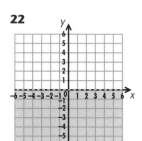

23

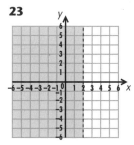

9 $y > 0$

10 $x > 3$, $y \le -4$

11 $x \le -1$, $y < 2$

12 $x < 4$, $y > 5$

13 $x \ge -4$, $y > -4$

14 $x \le 5$, $y < 5$

15 $x \ge 0$, $y > 2$

16

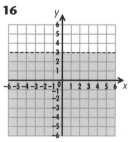

17

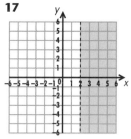

24

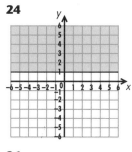

25

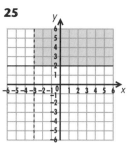

18

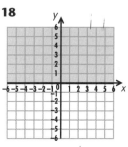

19

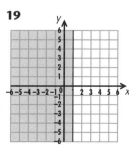

26

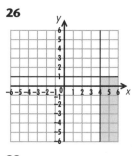

27

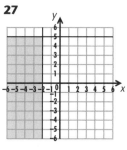

20

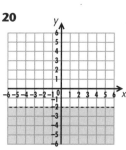

21

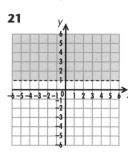

28

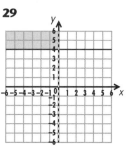

29

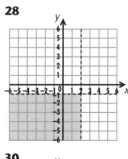

22

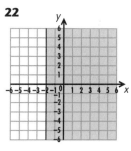

23

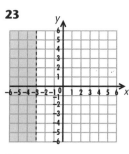

30

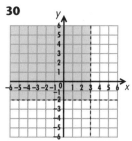

Exercise 40B

1 $y \ge -4$

2 $x < -2$

3 $x \ge -5$

4 $y < 1$

5 $x \ge -3$

6 $y \le -1$

7 $x \le 2$

8 $x < 5$

24

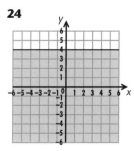

25

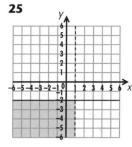

26

27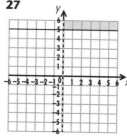

13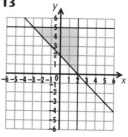

14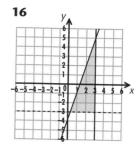

28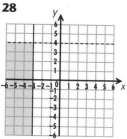

29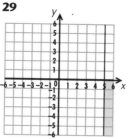

15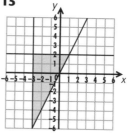

16

30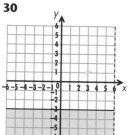

17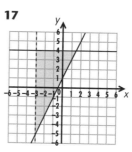

18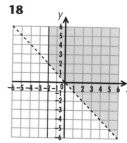

Exercise 40C

1 $y \leq x + 1, \ x \leq 4$

2 $y \leq -x, \ x \geq -4$

3 $y < 2, \ y \leq x - 1$

4 $y \leq 2 - x, \ x \geq -3, \ y \geq -3$

5 $y \leq x + 3, \ y \leq 3, \ x < 3$

6 $y \geq x + 1, \ y > 4$

7 $y \leq 2x, \ y < 2, \ x \leq 4$

8 $y < 2x + 1, \ y < 5, \ x \leq 5$

9 $y \leq x, \ x \leq 5, \ y \geq -4$

10 $y \leq \frac{1}{2}x + 2, \ x > -2, \ y > -3$

19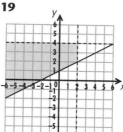

20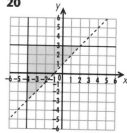

Exercise 40D

1 $y \geq x - 3, \ y \leq 2$

2 $y \leq x + 1, \ x \geq -3$

3 $y \leq 4 - x, \ x > -2, \ y > 2$

4 $y \leq x + 1, \ x < 2$

5 $y \leq x, \ y \leq 3$

6 $y \geq 1, \ x \leq 2, \ y > 2x$

7 $y \leq 2x + 1, \ y > -3, \ x < 2$

8 $y < -x, \ x \leq 3$

9 $y \geq 3x + 1, \ y < 2, \ x > -5$

10 $y > -x - 4, \ x \leq -1, \ y > -1$

11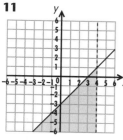

12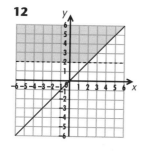

11

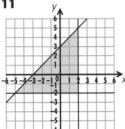

12

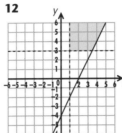

13

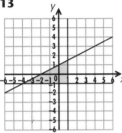

14

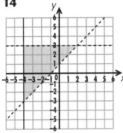

15

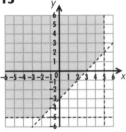

16

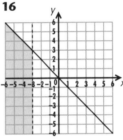

17

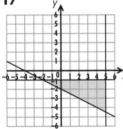

18

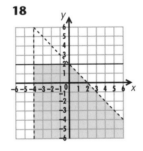

19

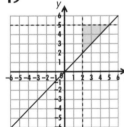

20

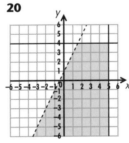

Exercise D

1   (a) 9   (b) −1   (c) −1   (d) 2

    (e) −3   (f) $\frac{1}{5}$

2   (a) 5.46, −1.46   (b) −0.63, −2.37   (c) 4.28

3   (a) $x = 8$, $y = 2$ (b) $x = \frac{1}{2}$, $y = 1$

    (c) $x = 6$, $y = 1$ (d) $x = 3$, $y = -3$

4   (a) $y = 2x - 2$ (b) $y = -x + 2$ (c) $y = \frac{1}{2}x$

5

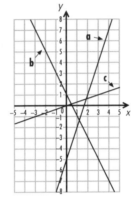

6 (a)

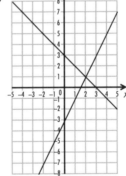

$x = 2$, $y = 1$

(b)

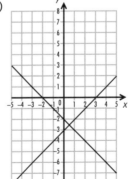

$x = 0.5$, $y = -2.5$

7 (a)

x	−2	−1	0	1	2	3	4	5
x^2	4	1	0	1	4	9	16	25
$-3x$	6	3	0	−3	−6	−9	−12	−15
−6	−6	−6	−6	−6	−6	−6	−6	−6
y	4	−2	−6	−8	−8	−6	−2	4

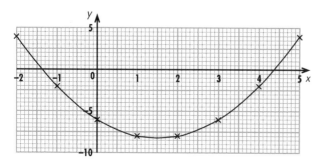

(b) −8.25   (c) −7.25   (d) 4.70, −1.70
(e) 4.37, −1.37   (f) 3.79, −0.79

8

x	−3	−2	−1	0	1	2	3	4
x^3	−27	−8	−1	0	1	8	27	64
$-x^2$	−9	−4	−1	0	−1	−4	−9	−16
$-5x$	15	10	5	0	−5	−10	−15	−20
y	−21	−2	3	0	−5	−6	3	28

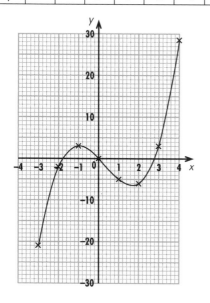

9

x	−4	−3	−2	−1	1	2	3	4
$\dfrac{6}{x}$	−1.5	−2	−3	−6	6	3	2	1.5

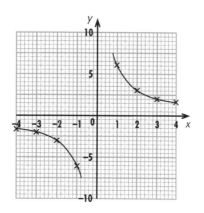

10 (a) $x \geq 3$ (b) $x < 2$ (c) $1 < x < 5$

11 (a)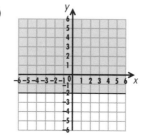

(b)

(c)

12 (a) $x < 3$ (b) $y > 2$, $x \geq 3$
(c) $y \leq x + 1$, $x \leq 4$, $y > -4$

13 (a)

(b)

(c)

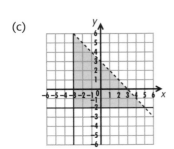

Exercise ▷▷

1 Jan £13.70, Jeremy £7.40

2 18 years old

3 (a) $x + x + 3 + x + x + 3 = 46$
   (b) $4x + 6 = 46$; $x = 10$

4 Apple 60 g, pear 30 g, orange 53 g

5 £6, £4

6 16p, 20p

7 17 cm, 9 cm

8 (a) 1100   (b) 15 m.p.h.   (c) $1\frac{1}{2}$ h
   (d) 1500   (e) 24 m.p.h.   (f) 96 miles

Shape, space and measures

41 BEARINGS

Exercise 41A
1 (a) 180° (b) 045° (c) 270° (d) 225°
2 (a) 067° (b) 155° (c) 258° (d) 318°
  (e) 146° (f) 207° (g) 162° (h) 280°
3 (a) 247° (b) 335° (c) 78° (d) 138°
  (e) 326° (f) 27° (g) 342° (h) 100°
4 (a) 230° (b) 295° (c) 102° (d) 353°
  (e) 120° (f) 325°
5 (a) 050° (b) 115° (c) 230° (d) 115°

Exercise 41B
1 (a) 090° (b) 135° (c) 315° (d) 000°
2 (a) 048° (b) 312° (c) 105° (d) 216°
  (e) 99° (f) 243° (g) 080° (h) 290°
3 (a) 228° (b) 132° (c) 285° (d) 36°
  (e) 279° (f) 63° (g) 260° (h) 110°
4 (a) 110° (b) 201° (c) 348° (d) 129°
  (e) 182° (f) 077°
5 (a) 140° (b) 218° (c) 281° (d) 101°

42 PYTHAGORAS' THEOREM: FINDING THE HYPOTENUSE

Exercise 42A
1 20 cm   2 13 m   3 12.2 cm
4 50 cm   5 2.01 m   6 70 mm
7 3.5 m   8 14.4 cm   9 9.22 cm
10 39 mm   11 2.5 m   12 5.66 cm
13 1.34 m   14 16.2 m   15 13.9 m
16 62.2 mm   17 9.22 cm   18 41 paces
19 8.43 m   20 7.00 m   21 80 mm
22 7.21 cm   23 13 m   24 36.1 cm

Exercise 42B
1 26 cm   2 25 m   3 17 cm
4 12.7 cm   5 69.5 mm   6 1.21 m
7 202 mm   8 15 cm   9 7.07 m
10 130 mm   11 15.6 m   12 10.8 cm
13 3.11 m   14 1.90 m   15 121 mm
16 52 mm   17 8.94 km   18 13 cm
19 36.4 cm   20 75 mm   21 14.1 cm
22 2.02 m   23 2.83 cm   24 17 cm

43 PYTHAGORAS' THEOREM: FINDING A LENGTH GIVEN THE HYPOTENUSE

Exercise 43A
1 20 cm   2 12 m   3 17.3 cm
4 3.87 cm   5 14.3 mm   6 0.583 m
7 0.933 m   8 30 cm   9 10 mm
10 5.08 m   11 34.6 mm   12 245 mm
13 1.56 m   14 8.06 cm   15 12.6 m
16 15.2 cm   17 39.4 cm   18 50 cm
19 12 cm   20 80 cm   21 15 cm
22 35.7 km   23 7 cm   24 35 cm

Exercise 43B
1 4 m   2 24 cm   3 8.31 cm
4 4.47 m   5 15.9 mm   6 4.44 m
7 250 mm   8 16 cm   9 40 mm
10 32.9 cm   11 9.22 cm   12 69.4 mm
13 56.6 m   14 1.44 m   15 51.2 cm
16 135 mm   17 60.2 cm   18 29 cm
19 22.4 km   20 24 cm   21 31 m
22 18 cm   23 67 cm   24 120 mm

44 PYTHAGORAS' THEOREM: MIXED EXAMPLES

Exercise 44A
1 15 m   2 5 cm   3 11.3 m
4 8.60 m   5 26.5 cm   6 38.0 mm
7 17.3 cm   8 99.3 mm   9 3.22 m
10 12.0 cm   11 31.6 mm   12 20.8 m
13 20.7 cm   14 5.48 cm   15 34.0 mm
16 66.1 mm   17 0.8 m   18 265 mm
19 Acute   20 Right-angled
21 Obtuse   22 Acute
23 Acute   24 Right-angled

Exercise 44B
1 25 cm   2 16 cm   3 12.2 m
4 12 m   5 1.19 m   6 12.8 cm
7 46.9 mm   8 2.06 m   9 130 mm
10 8.35 cm   11 44.3 cm   12 4.36 m
13 20.2 m   14 39.7 cm   15 5.77 m
16 62.0 mm   17 0.781 m   18 52 cm
19 Acute   20 Acute

21 Obtuse   **22** Right-angled

23 Acute   **24** Obtuse

Exercise 44C

1 39.4 cm   **2** 8.49 cm   **3** 71.1 mm

4 $x = 24.5$ cm, $y = 51.2$ cm

5 14.2 cm   **6** 9.17 cm   **7** 3.46 cm

8 8.06 cm   **9** 20 cm   **10** 4.5 km

11 31.8 cm   **12** 10.9 cm   **13** $p = 12$

14 10 cm   **15** 7 m

Exercise 44D

1 1.41 m   **2** 5.02 m   **3** 13.6 cm

4 34 cm (Note: Shortest, to 1 cm)

5 9.8 nautical miles

6 $p = 21.2$ cm, $q = 13.2$ cm

7 7.7 cm   **8** 106 mm   **9** 7.07 cm

10 3.61 cm   **11** 121 mm   **12** 3 cm

13 $a = 12.2$ cm, $b = 13.3$ cm

14 6.71 m   **15** 20 cm

45 SIMILARITY (1)

Exercise 45A

1 $x = 165$ mm, $y = 15$ cm

2 $x = 27$ mm, $y = 46$ mm

3 Not similar

4 $x = 11.25$ cm, $y = 12.8$ cm

5 $x = 39$ mm, $y = 38.5$ mm

6 $x = 26$ mm

$y = 26.7$ mm (3 s.f.)

7 Yes

8 Yes

9 No

10 No

11 No

12 Yes

13 PR = 12 cm, QR = 14 cm

14 PR = 116 mm, QR = 68 mm

15 AB = 40 mm, AC = 32 mm

16 PR = 32 cm, PQ = 24 cm

17 AB = 126 mm, BC = 75 mm

18 PR = 96 mm, PQ = 126 mm

Exercise 45B

1 $x = 13$ cm, $y = 14$ cm

2 Not similar

3 $x = 37$ mm, $y = 28$ mm

4 $x = 8.7$ cm, $y = 12.3$ cm

5 $x = 126.4$ mm, $y = 86.4$ mm

6 $x = 2.1$ m, $y = 2.6$ m

7 Yes

8 Yes

9 No

10 No

11 Yes

12 Yes

13 PR = 10.5 cm, QR = 6 cm

14 AB = 6 cm, BC = 8 cm

15 PR = 6.25 cm, PQ = 3.75 cm

16 PR = 24 mm, PQ = 32 mm

17 PR = 4.5 cm, QR = 5 cm

18 PR = 4 cm, PQ = 2.5 cm

46 SIMILARITY (2)

Exercise 46A

1 (a) Triangles ABC and ADE   (b) 1 : 4
(c) AE = 88 mm, CE = 66 mm, AD = 116 mm

2 (a) Triangles WXO and ZYO   (b) 1 : 2
(c) OW = 40 mm, OX = 58 mm, XY = 176 mm

3 (a) Triangles EFG and EHI   (b) 1 : 3
(c) HI = 129 mm, EF = 42 mm, EH = 126 mm

4 (a) Triangles JKO and MLO   (b) 1 : 3
(c) LM = 147 cm, JO = 47 cm, JM = 188 cm

5 (a) Triangles POQ and TOS   (b) 2 : 3
(c) OS = 5.7 cm, OT = 6.3 cm, PT = 10.5 cm

6 (a) Triangles ABE and ACD   (b) 1 : 3
(c) AC = 36 cm, AD = 30 cm, BC = 24 cm

7 (a) Triangles MNO and MPQ   (b) 1 : 2
(c) OQ = 4 cm, NP =7.5 cm, MQ = 8 cm

8 (a) Triangles HOI and GOF   (b) 2 : 3
(c) FO = 57 mm, GO =117 mm, FI = 95 mm

Exercise 46B

1 (a) Triangles IJH and IFG   (b) 1 : 2
(c) FI = 17 cm, HI = 5 cm, FJ = 8.5 cm

2 (a) Triangles ABO and DCO   (b) 1 : 3
(c) CD = 66 mm, BO = 18 mm, AD = 80 mm

3 (a) Triangles CDO and FEO   (b) 2 : 3
(c) EF = 45 mm, ED = 105 mm, EO = 63 mm

4 (a) Triangles AEB and ADC   (b) 1 : 3
(c) AD = 150 mm, DE = 100 mm, BE = 80 mm

5 (a) Triangles AOB and YOX   (b) 2 : 3
(c) AO = 8 cm, AB = 7 cm, AY = 20 cm

6 (a) Triangles STX and SUV   (b) 1 : 2
(c) SX = 6 cm, TU = 7.5 cm, SV = 12 cm

7 (a) Triangles QPR and SPT   (b) 1 : 4
(c) PT = 128 mm, PS = 152 mm, QS = 114 mm

8 (a) Triangles DEO and GFO   (b) 1 : 2
(c) FO = 64 mm, DO = 24 mm, GO = 48 mm

TRIGONOMETRY: NAMING SIDES AND STATING TRIGONOMETRIC RATIOS

Exercise 47A

1 $\text{Sin } A = \dfrac{BC}{AB}$, $\cos A = \dfrac{AC}{AB}$, $\tan A = \dfrac{BC}{AC}$

$\text{Sin } B = \dfrac{AC}{AB}$, $\cos B = \dfrac{BC}{AB}$, $\tan B = \dfrac{AC}{BC}$

2 $\text{Sin } E = \dfrac{DF}{EF}$, $\cos E = \dfrac{DE}{EF}$, $\tan E = \dfrac{DF}{DE}$

$\text{Sin } F = \dfrac{DE}{EF}$, $\cos F = \dfrac{DF}{EF}$, $\tan F = \dfrac{DE}{DF}$

3 $\text{Sin } H = \dfrac{GI}{HI}$, $\cos H = \dfrac{GH}{HI}$, $\tan H = \dfrac{GI}{GH}$

$\text{Sin } I = \dfrac{GH}{HI}$, $\cos I = \dfrac{GI}{HI}$, $\tan I = \dfrac{GH}{GI}$

4 $\text{Sin } J = \dfrac{KL}{JK}$, $\cos J = \dfrac{JL}{JK}$, $\tan J = \dfrac{KL}{JL}$

$\text{Sin } K = \dfrac{JL}{JK}$, $\cos K = \dfrac{KL}{JK}$, $\tan K = \dfrac{JL}{KL}$

5 $\text{Sin } M = \dfrac{NO}{MN}$, $\cos M = \dfrac{MO}{MN}$, $\tan M = \dfrac{NO}{MO}$

$\text{Sin } N = \dfrac{MO}{MN}$, $\cos N = \dfrac{NO}{MN}$, $\tan N = \dfrac{MO}{NO}$

6 $\text{Sin } P = \dfrac{QR}{PQ}$, $\cos P = \dfrac{PR}{PQ}$, $\tan P = \dfrac{QR}{PR}$

$\text{Sin } Q = \dfrac{PR}{PQ}$, $\cos Q = \dfrac{QR}{PQ}$, $\tan Q = \dfrac{PR}{QR}$

7 $\text{Sin } S = \frac{4}{5}$, $\cos S = \frac{3}{5}$, $\tan S = \frac{4}{3}$

$\text{Sin } U = \frac{3}{5}$, $\cos U = \frac{4}{5}$, $\tan U = \frac{3}{4}$

8 $\text{Sin } W = \frac{57}{95} = \frac{3}{5}$, $\cos W = \frac{76}{95} = \frac{4}{5}$, $\tan W = \frac{57}{76} = \frac{3}{4}$

$\text{Sin } X = \frac{76}{95} = \frac{4}{5}$, $\cos X = \frac{57}{95} = \frac{3}{5}$, $\tan X = \frac{76}{57} = \frac{4}{3}$

9 $\text{Sin } A = \frac{65}{97}$, $\cos A = \frac{72}{97}$, $\tan A = \frac{65}{72}$

$\text{Sin } B = \frac{72}{97}$, $\cos B = \frac{65}{97}$, $\tan B = \frac{72}{65}$

10 $\text{Sin } E = \frac{45}{53}$, $\cos E = \frac{28}{53}$, $\tan E = \frac{45}{28}$

$\text{Sin } F = \frac{28}{53}$, $\cos F = \frac{45}{53}$, $\tan F = \frac{28}{45}$

11 $\text{Sin } G = \frac{60}{109}$, $\cos G = \frac{91}{109}$, $\tan G = \frac{60}{91}$

$\text{Sin } H = \frac{91}{109}$, $\cos H = \frac{60}{109}$, $\tan H = \frac{91}{60}$

12 $\text{Sin } J = \frac{4}{5}$, $\cos J = \frac{3}{5}$, $\tan J = \frac{4}{3}$

$\text{Sin } L = \frac{3}{5}$, $\cos L = \frac{4}{5}$, $\tan L = \frac{3}{4}$

13 $\text{Tan } A = \frac{7}{5} = 1.4$, $\tan B = \frac{5}{7} = 0.714$

14 $\text{Sin } E = \cos F = \frac{11}{20} = 0.55$

15 $\text{Tan } G = \frac{6}{9} = 0.667$, $\tan I = \frac{9}{6} = 1.5$

16 $\text{Sin } J = \cos L = \frac{15}{25} = 0.6$

17 $\text{Cos } M = \sin N = \frac{25}{50} = 0.5$

18 $\text{Tan } P = \frac{7}{9} = 0.778$, $\tan R = \frac{9}{7} = 1.29$

19 $\text{Tan } S = \frac{6}{6} = 1$, $\tan T = \frac{6}{6} = 1$

20 $\text{Sin } V = \cos W = \frac{5}{13} = 0.385$

Exercise 47B

1 $\text{Sin } B = \dfrac{AC}{BC}$, $\cos B = \dfrac{AB}{BC}$, $\tan B = \dfrac{AC}{AB}$

$\text{Sin } C = \dfrac{AB}{BC}$, $\cos C = \dfrac{AC}{BC}$, $\tan C = \dfrac{AB}{AC}$

2 $\text{Sin } D = \dfrac{EF}{DE}$, $\cos D = \dfrac{DF}{DE}$, $\tan D = \dfrac{EF}{DF}$

$\text{Sin } E = \dfrac{DF}{DE}$, $\cos E = \dfrac{EF}{DE}$, $\tan E = \dfrac{DF}{EF}$

3 $\text{Sin } G = \dfrac{HI}{GI}$, $\cos G = \dfrac{GH}{GI}$, $\tan G = \dfrac{HI}{GH}$

$\text{Sin } I = \dfrac{GH}{GI}$, $\cos I = \dfrac{HI}{HI}$, $\tan I = \dfrac{GH}{HI}$

4 $\text{Sin } K = \dfrac{JL}{KL}$, $\cos K = \dfrac{JK}{KL}$, $\tan K = \dfrac{JL}{JK}$

$\text{Sin } L = \dfrac{JK}{KL}$, $\cos L = \dfrac{JL}{KL}$, $\tan L = \dfrac{JK}{JL}$

5 $\text{Sin } N = \dfrac{MO}{NO}$, $\cos N = \dfrac{MN}{NO}$, $\tan N = \dfrac{MO}{MN}$

$\text{Sin } O = \dfrac{MN}{NO}$, $\cos O = \dfrac{MO}{NO}$, $\tan O = \dfrac{MN}{MO}$

6 $\text{Sin } Q = \dfrac{PR}{QR}$, $\cos Q = \dfrac{PQ}{QR}$, $\tan Q = \dfrac{PR}{PQ}$

$\text{Sin } R = \dfrac{PQ}{QR}$, $\cos R = \dfrac{PR}{QR}$, $\tan R = \dfrac{PQ}{PR}$

7 $\text{Sin } S = \frac{8}{17}$, $\cos S = \frac{15}{17}$, $\tan S = \frac{8}{15}$

$\text{Sin } U = \frac{15}{17}$, $\cos U = \frac{8}{17}$, $\tan U = \frac{15}{8}$

8 $\text{Sin } W = \frac{3}{5}$, $\cos W = \frac{4}{5}$, $\tan W = \frac{3}{4}$

$\text{Sin } X = \frac{4}{5}$, $\cos X = \frac{3}{5}$, $\tan X = \frac{4}{3}$

9 $\text{Sin } A = \frac{21}{29}$, $\cos A = \frac{20}{29}$, $\tan A = \frac{21}{20}$

$\text{Sin } B = \frac{20}{29}$, $\cos B = \frac{21}{29}$, $\tan B = \frac{20}{21}$

10 $\text{Sin } D = \frac{51}{85} = \frac{3}{5}$, $\cos D = \frac{68}{85} = \frac{4}{5}$, $\tan D = \frac{51}{68} = \frac{3}{4}$

$\text{Sin } E = \frac{68}{85} = \frac{4}{5}$, $\cos E = \frac{51}{85} = \frac{3}{5}$, $\tan E = \frac{68}{51} = \frac{4}{3}$

11 $\text{Sin } H = \frac{33}{65}$, $\cos H = \frac{56}{65}$, $\tan H = \frac{33}{56}$

$\text{Sin } I = \frac{56}{65}$, $\cos I = \frac{33}{65}$, $\tan I = \frac{56}{33}$

12 $\sin K = \frac{76}{95} = \frac{4}{5}$, $\cos K = \frac{57}{95} = \frac{3}{5}$, $\tan K = \frac{76}{57} = \frac{4}{3}$

$\sin L = \frac{57}{95} = \frac{3}{5}$, $\cos L = \frac{76}{95} = \frac{4}{5}$, $\tan L = \frac{57}{76} = \frac{3}{4}$

13 $\sin B = \frac{7}{10} = 0.7$, $\cos C = \frac{7}{10} = 0.7$

14 $\cos D = \frac{16}{25} = 0.64$, $\sin F = \frac{16}{25} = 0.64$

15 $\tan H = \frac{5}{3} = 1.33$, $\tan I = \frac{3}{5} = 0.6$

16 $\sin J = \frac{5}{8} = 0.625$, $\cos K = \frac{5}{8} = 0.625$

17 $\tan M = \frac{12}{7} = 1.71$, $\tan N = \frac{7}{12} = 0.583$

18 $\cos P = \frac{24}{60} = 0.4$, $\sin R = \frac{24}{60} = 0.4$

19 $\sin S = \frac{3.2}{5} = 0.64$, $\cos T = \frac{3.2}{5} = 0.64$

20 $\tan V = \frac{4}{27} = 0.148$, $\tan X = \frac{27}{4} = 6.75$

48 TRIGONOMETRY: FINDING UNKNOWN ANGLES

Exercise 48A

1 $\sin E = \cos G = \frac{3}{8}$; $E = 22.0°$, $G = 68°$

2 $\tan H = \frac{5}{6}$ or $\tan I = \frac{6}{5}$; $H = 39.8°$, $I = 50.2°$

3 $\cos L = \sin M = \frac{1.5}{6}$; $L = 75.5°$, $M = 14.5°$

4 $\sin N = \cos P = \frac{17}{20}$; $N = 58.2°$, $P = 31.2°$

5 $\tan Q = \frac{84}{70}$ or $\tan S = \frac{70}{84}$; $L = 50.2°$, $M = 39.8°$

6 $\sin T = \cos U = \frac{1.95}{2.75}$; $T = 45.2°$, $U = 44.8°$

7 $\cos X = \sin Y = \frac{42}{67}$; $X = 51.2°$, $Y = 38.8°$

8 $\tan A = \frac{145}{95}$ or $\tan B = \frac{95}{145}$; $A = 56.8°$, $B = 33.2°$

9 (a) $\sin P = \cos Q = \frac{3}{10}$ (b) $P = 17.5°$, $Q = 72.5°$

10 (a) $\cos P = \sin Q = \frac{55}{120}$ (b) $P = 27.3°$, $Q = 62.7°$

11 (a) $\tan P = 2$ or $\tan Q = \frac{1}{2}$
(b) $P = 26.6°$, $Q = 63.4°$

12 (a) $\tan P = \frac{20}{25}$ or $\tan Q = \frac{25}{20}$
(b) $P = 38.7°$, $Q = 51.3°$

13 (a) $\cos P = \sin Q = \frac{16}{25}$ (b) $P = 50.2°$, $Q = 39.8°$

14 (a) $\tan P = \frac{27}{50}$ or $\tan Q = \frac{50}{27}$
(b) $P = 28.4°$, $Q = 61.6°$

15 (a) $\tan P = \frac{18}{125}$ or $\tan Q = \frac{125}{18}$
(b) $P = 8.2°$, $Q = 91.8°$

16 (a) $\sin P = \cos Q = \frac{13}{29}$ (b) $P = 26.6°$, $Q = 63.4°$

Exercise 48B

1 $\sin G = \cos H = \frac{22}{50}$; $G = 26.1°$, $H = 63.9°$

2 $\tan J = \frac{3.6}{2.4}$ or $\tan K = \frac{2.4}{3.6}$; $J = 56.3°$, $K = 33.7°$

3 $\cos N = \sin O = \frac{65}{100}$; $N = 49.5°$, $O = 40.5°$

4 $\sin P = \cos R = \frac{8}{11}$; $P = 46.7°$, $R = 43.3°$

5 $\tan S = \frac{8}{3}$ or $\tan U = \frac{3}{8}$; $S = 69.4°$, $U = 20.6°$

6 $\cos W = \sin X = \frac{10.1}{14.2}$; $W = 44.7°$, $X = 45.3°$

7 $\cos B = \sin C = \frac{75}{105}$; $B = 44.4°$, $C = 45.6°$

8 $\tan D = \frac{1.72}{2.14}$ or $\tan E = \frac{2.14}{1.72}$; $D = 38.8°$, $E = 51.2°$

9 (a) $\tan P = \frac{40}{32}$ or $\tan Q = \frac{32}{40}$
(b) $P = 51.3°$, $Q = 38.7°$

10 (a) $\cos P = \sin Q = \frac{45}{50}$ (b) $P = 64.2°$, $Q = 25.8°$

11 (a) $\sin P = \cos Q = \frac{8}{25}$ (b) $P = 18.7°$, $Q = 71.3°$

12 (a) $\tan P = \frac{18}{8}$ or $\tan Q = \frac{8}{18}$
(b) $P = 66.0°$, $Q = 24.0°$

13 (a) $\cos P = \sin Q = \frac{23}{80}$ (b) $P = 73.3°$, $Q = 16.7°$

14 (a) $\tan P = \frac{75}{95}$ or $\tan Q = \frac{95}{75}$
(b) $P = 38.3°$, $Q = 51.7°$

15 (a) $\tan P = \frac{3.4}{6.5}$ or $\tan Q = \frac{6.5}{3.4}$
(b) $P = 27.6°$, $Q = 62.4°$

16 (a) $\sin P = \cos Q = \frac{4.5}{8.5}$ (b) $P = 32.0°$, $Q = 58.0°$

49 TRIGONOMETRY: FINDING UNKNOWN LENGTHS

Exercise 49A

1 $\sin 38° = \frac{a}{10}$, $a = 6.16$ cm

2 $\tan 44° = \frac{b}{8}$, $b = 7.73$ cm

3 $\cos 32° = \frac{c}{25}$, $c = 21.2$ mm

4 $\tan 51° = \frac{d}{2.4}$, $d = 2.96$ m

5 $\cos 61° = \frac{e}{82}$, $e = 39.8$ mm

6 $\tan 29° = \frac{f}{32}$, $f = 17.7$ cm

7 $\sin 42° = \dfrac{g}{12}$, $g = 8.03$ cm;

$\cos 42° = \dfrac{h}{12}$, $h = 8.92$ cm

8 $\tan 19° = \dfrac{i}{43}$, $i = 14.8$ mm

9 $\sin 30° = \dfrac{AB}{7}$, $AB = 3.50$ cm

10 $\tan 44° = \dfrac{AB}{20}$, $AB = 19.3$ cm

11 $\cos 29.4° = \dfrac{AB}{100}$, $AB = 87.1$ mm;

$\sin 29.4° = \dfrac{BC}{100}$, $BC = 49.1$ mm

12 $\tan 12.7° = \dfrac{7.5}{BC}$, $BC = 33.3$ cm

13 $\tan 60° = \dfrac{BC}{95}$, $BC = 165$ mm;

$\cos 60° = \dfrac{95}{AC}$, $AC = 190$ mm

14 $\tan 44° = \dfrac{BC}{25}$, $BC = 24.1$ cm

15 $\sin 58.5° = \dfrac{2.8}{AC}$, $AC = 3.28$ m;

$\tan 31.5° = \dfrac{AB}{2.8}$, $AB = 1.72$ m

16 $\sin 72.8° = \dfrac{AB}{112}$, $AB = 107$ mm;

$\cos 72.8° = \dfrac{BC}{112}$, $BC = 33.1$ mm

Exercise 49B

1 $\tan 56° = \dfrac{p}{4}$, $p = 5.93$ m

2 $\cos 40° = \dfrac{q}{12}$, $q = 9.19$ cm

3 $\sin 24° = \dfrac{r}{20}$, $r = 8.13$ cm

4 $\tan 53° = \dfrac{s}{1.5}$, $s = 1.99$ m

5 $\tan 26° = \dfrac{t}{15}$, $t = 7.32$ cm

6 $\sin 17° = \dfrac{u}{40}$, $u = 11.7$ cm;

$\cos 17° = \dfrac{v}{40}$, $v = 38.3$ cm

7 $\sin 43° = \dfrac{w}{3.2}$, $w = 2.18$ m;

$\cos 43° = \dfrac{x}{3.2}$, $x = 2.34$ m

8 $\tan 51° = \dfrac{y}{18}$, $y = 22.2$ cm

9 $\tan 60° = \dfrac{BC}{12}$, $BC = 20.8$ cm

10 $\sin 25° = \dfrac{AB}{30}$, $AB = 12.7$ cm;

$\cos 25° = \dfrac{BC}{30}$, $BC = 27.2$ cm

11 $\sin 50° = \dfrac{BC}{45}$, $BC = 34.5$ mm

12 $\tan 47.5° = \dfrac{BC}{5.4}$, $BC = 5.89$ m

13 $\sin 7.5° = \dfrac{AB}{75}$, $AB = 9.79$ mm;

$\cos 7.5° = \dfrac{BC}{75}$, $BC = 74.4$ mm

14 $\cos 82° = \dfrac{3.95}{AC}$, $AC = 28.4$ m;

$\tan 82° = \dfrac{BC}{3.95}$, $BC = 28.1$ m

15 $\tan 38.6° = \dfrac{AB}{22}$, $AB = 17.6$ cm;

$\cos 38.6° = \dfrac{22}{AC}$, $AC = 28.2$ cm

16 $\cos 40° = \dfrac{AB}{157}$, $AB = 120$ mm;

$\sin 40° = \dfrac{BC}{157}$, $BC = 101$ mm

50 TRIGONOMETRY: MISCELLANEOUS PROBLEMS

Exercise 50A
1 35.3°, 54.7°
2 33.6°
3 42.4 m
4 5.7°
5 18.5°
6 17 m
7 44 cm
8 59.7°, 59.7° and 60.5/60.6°

9 (a)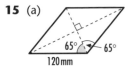
    33° 33° 9 cm

(b) 15.1 cm, 9.8 cm

10 (a) 6.93 km   (b) 4 km
11 42.8°
12 (a) 90°   (b)(i) 7.14 cm (ii) 9.65 cm
13 71.6
14 5.39 mm, 068°
15 17.0 cm
16 (a) 167°   (b) 9.43 km

Exercise 50B

1 1.20 m
2 42°
3 700 m
4 36.9°, 53.1°
5 (a) 11.3 km   (b) 4.10 km
6 7 m
7 7.13 m
8 2.4°
9 56.3°
10 (a) 90°   (b) 50 mm
11 30°
12 55.6°, 55.6° and 68.8°
13 (a) 26 cm   (b) 2 mm
14 3.35 mm, 026.6°

15 (a)
    65° 65° 120 mm

(b) 10.1 cm, 2.17 cm

16 (a) 320°   (b) 15.6 km

51 ENLARGEMENT: FRACTIONAL SCALE FACTORS

Exercise 51A

1
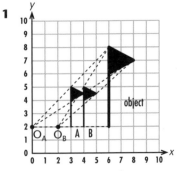
$O_A = (0, 2)$; S.F.$_A = \frac{1}{2}$
$O_B = (2, 2)$; S.F.$_B = \frac{1}{2}$

2
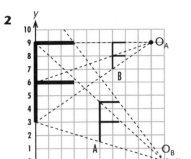
$O_A = (9, 9)$; S.F.$_A = \frac{1}{3}$ $O_B = (10, 0)$; S.F.$_B = \frac{1}{2}$

3
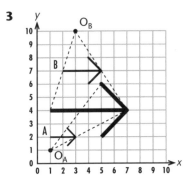
$O_A = (1, 1)$; S.F.$_A = \frac{1}{3}$ $O_B = (3, 10)$; S.F.$_B = \frac{1}{2}$

4
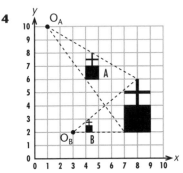
$O_A = (1, 10)$; S.F.$_A = \frac{1}{2}$ $O_B = (3, 2)$; S.F.$_B = \frac{1}{4}$

5
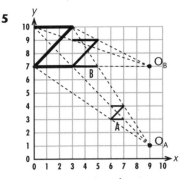
$O_A = (9, 1)$; S.F.$_A = \frac{1}{3}$ $O_B = (9, 7)$; S.F.$_B = \frac{2}{3}$

6

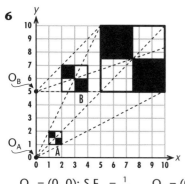

$O_A = (0, 0)$; S.F.$_A = \frac{1}{5}$ $O_B = (0, 5)$; S.F.$_B = \frac{2}{5}$

7

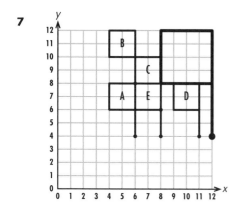

8

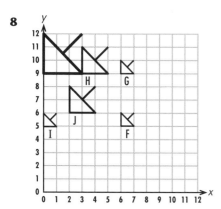

9

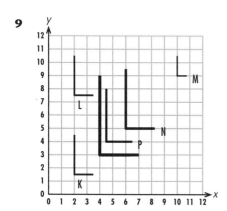

Exercise 51B

1

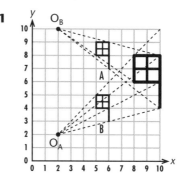

$O_A = (2, 2)$; S.F.$_A = \frac{1}{2}$ $O_B = (2, 10)$; S.F.$_B = \frac{1}{2}$

2

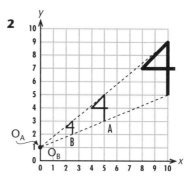

$O_A = (0, 1)$; S.F.$_A = \frac{1}{2}$ $O_B = (0, 1)$; S.F.$_B = \frac{1}{4}$

3

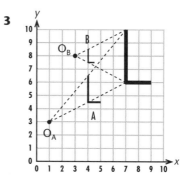

$O_A = (1, 3)$; S.F.$_A = \frac{1}{2}$ $O_B = (3, 8)$; S.F.$_B = \frac{1}{4}$

4

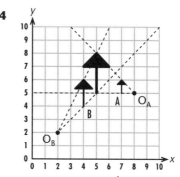

$O_A = (8, 5)$; S.F.$_A = \frac{1}{3}$ $O_B = (2, 2)$; S.F.$_B = \frac{2}{3}$

5

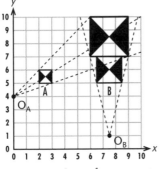

$O_A = (0, 4)$; S.F.$_A = \frac{1}{3}$ $O_B = (7.5, 1)$; S.F.$_B = \frac{2}{3}$

6

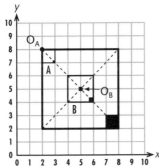

$O_A = (2, 8)$; S.F.$_A = \frac{1}{6}$ $O_B = (5, 5)$; S.F.$_B = \frac{1}{3}$

7

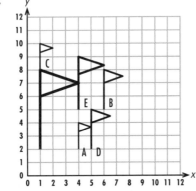

8

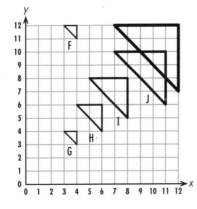

9

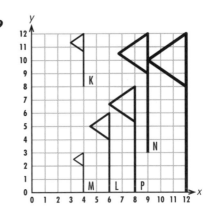

52 THE LOCUS OF A POINT

Exercise 52A

1 Circle of radius 5 cm

2

3 Angle bisector of RQS

4

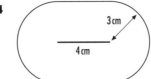

5

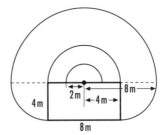

6

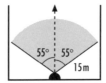

7

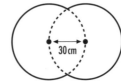

8

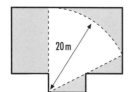

9

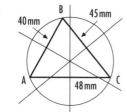

quadrants at corners

16 m × 28 m rectangle

3 m away

10

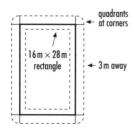

B
40 mm   45 mm
A   48 mm   C

Exercise 52B

1

45 mm

2 Perpendicular bisector of ST

3 Angle bisector of angle CAB

4

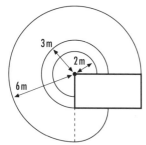

3 m
2 m
6 m

5

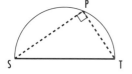

P
S   T

6

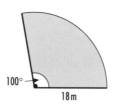

100°   18 m

7

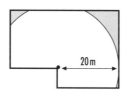

Smith   Jones
12 m   12 m
cable

8

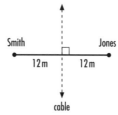

20 m

9

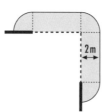

2 m

10

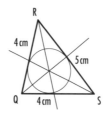

R
4 cm   5 cm
Q   4 cm   S

REVISION

Exercise E

1 (a) 077°   (b) 335°   (c) 217°   (d) 148°
2 (a) 257°   (b) 155°   (c) 037°   (d) 328°
3 (a) 8.54 cm   (b) 76.8 mm   (c) 2.92 m
4 (a) PR = 148 mm, QR = 136 mm
   (b) AB = 131 cm, PR = 270 cm
   (c) Not similar
5 (a) $A = 48.6°$, $B = 41.4°$
   (b) $c = 6.13$ cm, $d = 5.14$ cm
   (c) $e = 10.8$ cm, $f = 16.1$ cm
   (d) $G = 53.9°$, $H = 36.1°$

6 (a) (9, 9), S.F. = $\frac{1}{2}$ (b) (1, 4), S.F. = $\frac{2}{3}$

7 Angle bisector of angle BAC

8 Perpendicular bisector of ST

Exercise EE

1 (a) 072°   (b) 252°   (c) 072°   (d) 325°

2

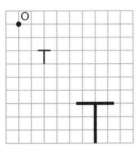

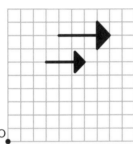

3 $x = 1.4\,\text{m}$, $y = 2.6\,\text{m}$

4 (a) ABC and ADE   (b) 26.7 cm

     (c) AE = 33.3 cm, CE = 18.3 cm

5 (a) 25.7 cm   (b) 35.2°

6 120°, 8.06 miles

7 14.8 cm

8 36.9°

9 35.6 m

10 7.00 km

11

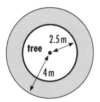

12

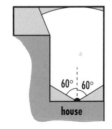

13

53 COMPOUND MEASURES

Exercise 53A

1 50 m.p.h.	**2** 5 kg/cm²
3 150 *l*	**4** 1.25 gal
5 200 cm³	**6** 31.8 litres
7 88 km	**8** 1.61 m/s
9 50 min	**10** 42 m.p.g.
11 0.0238 gal/mile	**12** 0.148 cm³
13 180 *l*/h	**14** 225 miles
15 58.6 m.p.h.	**16** 9 km/h

Exercise 53B

1 69 m.p.h.	**2** 22 km/*l*
3 26.7 km	**4** 3.70 g/cm³
5 1250 *l*/h	**6** 6 gal
7 20 min	**8** 261 miles
9 463 g	**10** 0.05 *l*/km
11 128 miles	**12** 2.96 g/cm³
13 42 s	**14** 547 g
15 (a) 1 h 20 min or 1.33 h	(b) 74.1 km/h
16 160 g/cm²	

54 AREA AND PERIMETER (1)

Exercise 54A

1 16.7 cm²

2 96 cm²

3 1.8 m²

4 17.85 cm²

5 1230 mm²

6 201 cm²

7 16 cm²

8 2.54 m²

9 37.7 cm

10 4.8 m

11 72 cm

12 157 mm

13 (a) 70 cm²   (b) 34 cm

14 (a) 1.69 m²   (b) 5.2 m

15 (a) 1000 cm^2 (b) 42 cm
16 (a) 28.4 cm^2 (b) 246 mm or 24.6 cm
17 (a) 4870 mm^2 (b) 300 mm
18 (a) 135 cm^2 (b) 54 cm
19 (a) 52.8 cm^2 (b) 34 cm
20 (a) 63.6 cm^2 (b) 28.3 cm

Exercise 54B

1 1.12 m^2
2 0.495 m^2
3 16.3 cm^2
4 57.8 cm^2
5 1120 mm^2 or 11.2 cm^2
6 78.5 cm^2
7 6360 mm^2
8 99 cm^2
9 128 mm
10 260 mm
11 141 mm
12 53.4 cm
13 (a) 66 cm^2 (b) 37.1 cm
14 (a) 68.3 cm^2 (b) 34 cm
15 (a) 24 cm^2 (b) 22 cm
16 (a) 27.5 cm^2 (b) 261 mm or 26.1 cm
17 (a) 0.81 m^2 (b) 3.6 m
18 (a) 7320 mm^2 (b) 384 mm
19 (a) 38.5 cm^2 (b) 25.6 cm
20 (a) 5540 mm^2 (b) 264 mm

55 AREA AND PERIMETER (2)

Exercise 55A

1 88 m^2
2 35 + 7.5 = 42.5 cm^2
3 63 + 77 = 140 cm^2
4 100 – 78.5 = 21.5 cm^2
5 24 m^2, 24 cm
6 1 060 mm^2, 81.7 + 52 = 133.7 or 134 mm
7 1.77 m^2, 2.36 + 3 = 5.36 m
8 504 + 150 = 654 cm^2, 120 cm
9 9.8 – 3.46 = 6.34 m^2
10 3118 – 2828 = 290 mm^2
11 (a) 34 cm by 22 cm   (b) 1260 – 748 = 512 cm^2
12 (a) 19.2 m   (b) 23.04 – 5.76 = 17.28 or 17.3 m^2
13 210 + 180 = 390 m
14 (a) 68 tiles   (b) 8320 cm^2 (c) 2450 cm^2
15 (a) 39.3 cm^2 (b) 39.3 cm^2 (c) Same
     (d) 37.7 cm

Exercise 55B

1 5.76 – 2.16 = 3.60 m^2
2 66 + 47.5 = 114 cm^2
3 114.75 – 43.20 = 71.55 or 71.6 cm^2
4 3840 + 3020 = 6860 mm^2
5 14.1 cm^2, 9.43 + 6 = 15.43 or 15.4 cm
6 20 + 20 = 40 cm^2, 26 cm
7 5.30 m^2, 3 + 7.07 = 10.07 or 10.1 m
8 117 + 30 = 147 cm^2, 48 cm
9 (a) 41.3 – 10 = 31.3 m^2 (b) 26 m
10 113 mm^2
11 (a) 16 mm   (b) 72.25 – 59.29 = 6.32 cm^2
12 270 + 212 = 482 cm (to the nearest 10 cm)
13 Area = 2500 – 490.9 = 2009 or 2010 mm^2;
     perimeter = 150 + 39.27 = 189 mm
14 616 – 216 = 400 mm^2
15 (a) 72.39 – 43.01 ≈ 29.4 m^2
     (b) 30.16 – 23.25 = 6.91 m

56 VOLUME: CUBES AND CUBOIDS

Exercise 56A

1 (a) 3600 cm^3 (b) 3380 cm^3 (c) 30 000 cm^3
     (d) 5.67 m^3 (e) 32 800 mm^3 (f) 4320 cm^3
2 (a) 288 cm^3 (b) 2.20 m^3
     (c) 53 800 mm^3 (d) 450 cm^3 or 450 000 mm^3
3 (a) 25 cm   (b) 2 m
4 50 cm
5 8 cm
6 11.1 cm
7 10 cm
8 9.28 cm
9 3 min 12 s
10 2 350 ml
11 6.4 cm
12 9600 cm^3
13 (a) 320 × 180 × 96 (cm)   (b) 600   (c) 5.53 m^3
14 1000 m
15 77.8 cm

Exercise 56B

1 (a) 2630 cm^3 (b) 244 000 mm^3
     (c) 17.6 cm^3 (d) 421 875 or 422 000 mm^3
     (e) 9.9 m^3 (f) 4030 cm^3
2 (a) 4400 cm^3 (b) 18 785 or 18 800 mm^3
     (c) 1.85 m^3 (d) 216 cm^3
3 (a) 12 cm   (b) 40 mm
4 27.8 cm
5 9 cm
6 80 cm

7 8 min 20 s

8 14 cm

9 7.94 cm

10 (a) 1130 cm^3 (b) 2.72 m^3

11 15.3 cm

12 (a) 150 000 cm^3 (b) 0.15 m^3 (c) 25 cm

13 47.0 cm

14 0.0518 m^3

15 (a) 1400   (b) 69.4 cm
    (c) 195 is better than 192   (d) 1170

57 VOLUME OF A PRISM

Exercise 57A

1 (a) 112 cm^3 (b) 384 cm^3
    (c) 26 000 cm^3 (d) 153 140 mm^3 or 153 cm^3
    (e) 1.01 m^3 (f) 184 cm^3

2 (a) 12 cm^2 (b) 5 cm   (c) 13.5 cm   (d) 4.5 cm

3 30 cm^3

4 125 cm^3

5 360 cm^3

6 116 cm^3

7 83.3 cm^2

8 62.3 cm^3

9 7.3 cm

10 8 cm

11 20 cm

12 480 cm^3

13 98.2 cm^3

14 (a) 30 cm^2 (b) 615 cm^3

Exercise 57B

1 (a) 25.3 cm^3 (b) 48 cm^3
    (c) 2 170 000 mm^3 or 2170 cm^3
    (d) 132 cm^3 (e) 101 cm^3 or 101 000 mm^3
    (f) 4.62 cm^3 or 4620 mm^3

2 (a) 4.2 cm^2 (b) 40 mm   (c) 14 mm
    (d) 50 cm^2

3 252 cm^3

4 4 cm

5 1850 mm^3

6 38.5 cm^2

7 245 cm^3

8 8.0 cm

9 360 cm^3

10 760 cm^3

11 7 cm

12 514 cm^3

13 942 or 943 cm^3

14 (a)(i) 1230 mm^2 (ii) 12.3 cm^2 (b) 76.3 cm^3

58 SURFACE AREA

Exercise 58A

1 (a) 199 cm^2 (b) 2610 mm^2 (c) 3740 mm^2
    (d) 1290 cm^2

2 228 cm^2

3 (a) 18 000 cm^2 (b) 1.8 m^2

4 150 cm^2

5 388 cm^2

6 152 cm^2

7 77.3 cm^2

8 8.64 m^2

9 8.1 m^2

10 350.4 cm^2

11 28.8 m^2

12 (a) 110 cm^2 (b) 552 cm^2

Exercise 58B

1 (a) 336 cm^2 (b) 2450 mm^2 (c) 1030 cm^2
    (d) 5300 cm^2

2 236 cm^2

3 2.6 m^2

4 332 cm^2

5 3750 mm^2

6 76 m^2

7 5.44 m^2

8 350 cm^2

9 22.6 cm^2

10 3.84 m^2

11 292 cm^2

12 (a) 117 cm^2 (b) 1980 cm^2

R EVISION

Exercise F

1 187.2 g

2 90 km

3 1.2 gal

4 (a)(i) 77 cm^2 (ii) 36 cm
    (b)(i) 912 mm^2 (ii) 126 mm
    (c)(i) 12.25 cm^2 (ii) 14 m
    (d)(i) 49.5 cm^2 (ii) 32.9 cm
    (e)(i) 113 cm^2 (ii) 37.7 cm
    (f)(i) 1.5 m^2 (ii) 6. 0 m

5 (a) 77.0 cm^2, 36.0 cm   (b) 380 mm^2, 78.6 mm

6 (a) 8.1 m^2 (b) 334 cm^2

7 (a) 248 cm^2 (b) 240 cm^3

8 294 cm^2, 343 cm^3

9 (a)(i) 288 cm^2 (ii) 384 cm^3
(b)(i) 360 cm^2 (ii) 300 cm^3

Exercise FF

1 46.2 m.p.h.

2 200 cm^3

3 53 s

4 (a) 10.8 m, so 3 packs   (b) 6.93 m^2
(c) 866 g, so 2 boxes

5 (a) 500 l or 500 000 cm^3
(b) 110 cm (109.89 cm)
(c) 543 l (543.48 l)
(d) 19.9 cm or 20 cm

6 BC = $\sqrt{300}$ = 17.3 cm, so perimeter = 47.3 cm
and area = 86.6 cm^2

7 (a) 1810 cm^3 (b) 181 g

8 (a) 25.1 cm^2 (b) 1510 cm^3

9 (a) 96 000 cm^3 (b) 854 400 g or 854.4 kg
(c) 3.14 mm^2 (d) 100
(e) 31 000 m

10 (a) 163 cm   (b) 11 100 cm^2
(c) 2148 × 80 = 172 000 cm^3

Handling data

MEAN, MODE, MEDIAN AND RANGE FOR GROUPED DATA

Exercise 59A

1 (a) Mean 3.65, median 4, mode 4, range 5.
(b) The dice is biased towards 4.

2 (a) Mean 6.76, mode 8, median 7, range 10
(b) Median, mode and range unchanged; mean = 6.64

3 (a) 467
(b) Mean 60.7, median $60 \leq m < 70$, maximum range 80
(c) $60 \leq m < 70$, a large number of pupils scored 60–70 marks.

4 (a) 17.5 kg
(b) (i) 27.8 kg (ii) $25 \leq W < 30$
(c) (i) $25 \leq W < 30$ kg (ii) 25 kg
(d) Most sacks are 25 kg or over but less than 30 kg
(e) 28.9 kg

5 (a) 29.3 s
(b) Frequencies 3, 2, 7, 4, 3, 2
(c) 29.4 s
(d) Mode is 37 s; this has no real meaning because it is just a coincidence that 37 occurred 3 times. The modal group is $25 \leq T < 30$ and this tells us that the most usual length of time was between these limits.

6 (a) E 56, D 63.5, C 71, B 78.5
(b) 67.3   (c) 67.3
(d) The means are identical but the spread is a little greater, for example the ranges are 15 and 30 marks.
(e) Prediction – halfway between C and D; actual results – in grade C.

Exercise 59B

1 (a) 2.59, 3   (b) 3
(c) Not very sensible – 2 and 3 are both modes.

2 (a) Mean £3.13, mode £5, median £2, range £9
(b) £5 occurs 17 times but £1 occurs 16 times and could be considered as a mode as well.
(c) Mean £2.91, mode £5, median £2, range £8; mode and median remain the same.

3 (a) £20.50   (b) 48.8p
(c) Median $40 \leq C < 50$p, maximum range 80p
(d) Two modal classes: $30 \leq C < 40$p and $40 \leq C < 50$p

4 (a) (i) 46.5 miles (ii) $40 \leq M < 50$ miles
(b) $40 \leq M < 50$ miles
(c) 60 miles
(d) 42.5 miles

5 (a) Paper 1 30.5, Paper 2 22.0
(b) The modal class for Paper 1 of $30 \leq m < 40$ and the mean of 30.5 are both significantly higher than the modal class of $20 \leq m < 30$ and the mean of 22.0 for Paper 2. The students achieved a higher standard in Paper 1 than in Paper 2.

6 (a) 18.6 min   (b) 3.86 min
(c) 34, 7, 2, 1 min
(d) 3, 7.5, 13, 653 min
(e) (i) 18.9 min (ii) 4.2 min
(f) The means are very close.
(g) (i) 651 min (ii) 13 min

INTERPRETING AND COMPARING FREQUENCY POLYGONS

Exercise 60A

1 (a) Untrue – 100 times
(b) Untrue – 64 spins against 100 for Gary
(c) Untrue – 1 head and 4 heads are still different.
(d) True

2 (a) Untrue – winter 123 days, summer 121 days
(b) True   (c) True
(d) Untrue – only 48 days

3 (a) True
(b) Untrue – It is not possible to read off the graph between the points.
(c) True
(d) Untrue – The highest plants are in the class interval $50 \leq h < 60$ mm.

4 (a) True   (b) True
(c) Untrue – Omar 550 km, Mary 615 km approx.
(d) Untrue – It is not possible to read off values between the points.

5

Frequency

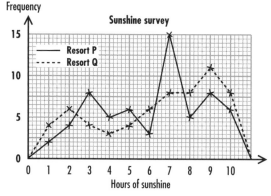

Sunshine survey

(a) Untrue – 'to the nearest hour' means that 30 min – 1 h 29 min would be rounded to 1 hour.
(b) True
(c) True
(d) Untrue – $\frac{15}{62}$ = 24.2%

6

Frequency

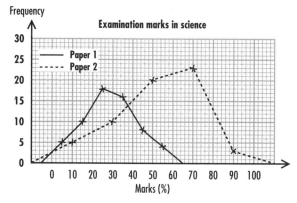

Examination marks in science

(a) Untrue – There are 61 candidates in each.
(b) True
(c) Untrue – 3 students scored 80–100% but it is not possible to read values except at points. So it is not possible to say if any students scored 100%.
(d) True

Exercise 60B

1 (a) True
(b) True
(c) Untrue – 68 goals in 1994, 84 goals in 1995
(d) Untrue – 34 in 1994, 23 in 1995

2 (a) True
(b) Untrue – Text A 113 words, Text B 115 words
(c) True
(d) Untrue – 167 letters

3 (a) Untrue – Stacey 86, Geoffrey 91
(b) Untrue – Stacey scores 90–120 thirty-four times.
(c) True
(d) Untrue – Maximum possible score for Stacey, taking upper limit of each class interval, is over 9000 but minimum possible score for Geoffrey, taking lowest value in class interval, is about 6500.

4 (a) True
(b) True
(c) Untrue – There is no significance between points on the graph.
(d) True

5

Frequency

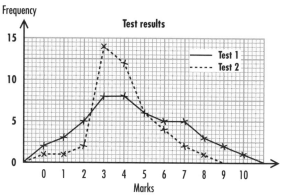

Test results

(a) Untrue – Test 1 48, Test 2 43
(b) Untrue – Highest score was 8 but the test could have been marked out of 10.
(c) True
(d) True

6

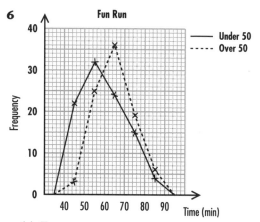

Fun Run

(a) True
(b) Untrue – Under 50s 97, Over 50s 89
(c) Untrue – There is no significance of the lines except at the points.
(d) True

Exercise 61A

1 (a)

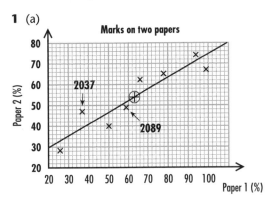

(b) (63.6, 54)
(f) (i) 63% or 64% (ii) 56% or 57%
(g) Positive correlation

2 (a)

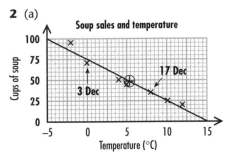

(b) Mean temperature 5.3°C, mean sales 49 cups
(f) (i) 15°C (ii) 100 cups
(g) Negative correlation

3 (a)

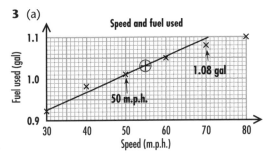

(b) Mean speed 55 m.p.h., mean fuel 1.03 gal
(f) (i) 1.07 gal (ii) 47.7 m.p.h.
(g) Positive correlation

4 (a)

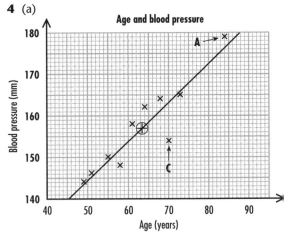

(b) Mean age 63.3 y, mean blood pressure 157 mm
(f) (i) 172–3 mm (ii) 45–6 y
(g) Positive correlation

5 (a)

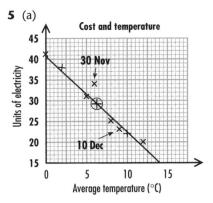

(b) Mean temp 6.5°C, mean number of units 29.25
(f) (i) 3°C (ii) 22–3 units
(g) Negative correlation

6 (a)

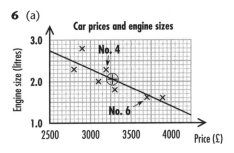

(b) Mean price £3270, mean engine size 2.06 *l*
(f) (i) 2.7–2.8 *l* (ii) £3900
(g) Negative correlation

Exercise 61B

1 (a)

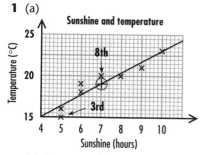

Sunshine and temperature

(b) Mean sunshine 7 hours, mean temperature 19°C

(f) (i) 23°C (ii) 4 hours

(g) Positive correlation

2 (a)

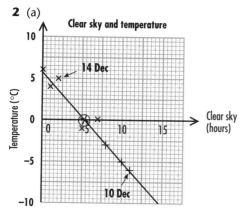

Clear sky and temperature

(b) Mean clear sky 5.5 hours, mean temperature 0°C

(f) (i) −6.5°C (ii) 7 h

(g) Negative correlation

3 (a)

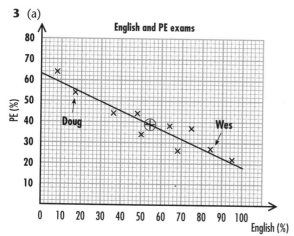

English and PE exams

(b) Mean English mark 54.5%, mean PE mark 39%

(f) (i) 30% (ii) 20%

(g) Negative correlation

4 (a)

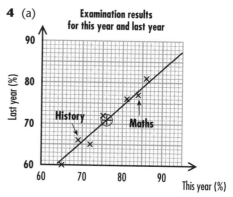

Examination results for this year and last year

(b) Mean marks – this year 76%, last year 71%

(f) (i) 64% (ii) 84%

(g) Positive correlation

5 (a)

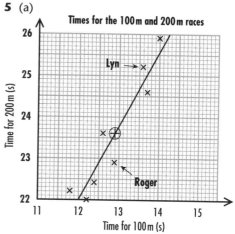

Times for the 100 m and 200 m races

(b) Mean 100 m time 12.9 s, mean 200 m time 23.6 s

(f) (i) 13.7 s (ii) 23.8 s

(g) Positive correlation

6 (a)

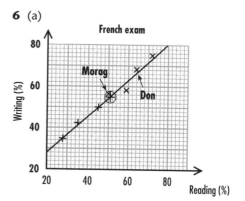

French exam

(b) Mean reading 50.4%, mean writing 54.9%

(f) (i) 56% (ii) 46%

(g) Positive correlation

Exercise 62A

1

Absences Upper limit	Cumulative frequency
5	4
10	9
15	14
19	18
25	22
30	25
35	27
40	28
45	29

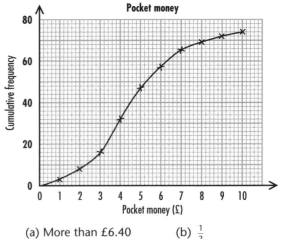

Pocket money

(a) More than £6.40   (b) $\frac{1}{2}$

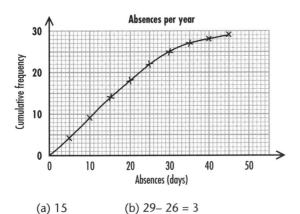

Absences per year

(a) 15   (b) 29– 26 = 3

3

Time (min) Upper limit	Cumulative frequency
2	8
4	26
6	60
8	108
10	153
12	187
14	212
16	229
18	239
20	246
22	249
24	250

2

Pocket money Upper limit	Cumulative frequency
£1	3
£2	8
£3	16
£4	32
£5	47
£6	57
£7	65
£8	69
£9	72
£10	74

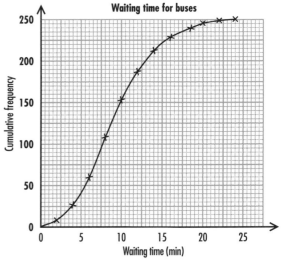

Waiting time for buses

(a) 220   (b) 9 min or less

4

Account Upper limit	Cumulative frequency
£100	2
£200	5
£300	10
£400	17
£500	25
£600	31
£700	35
£800	38
£900	40
£1000	41

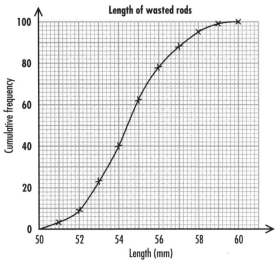

(a) 54.4 mm or less   (b) 100 – 82 = 18

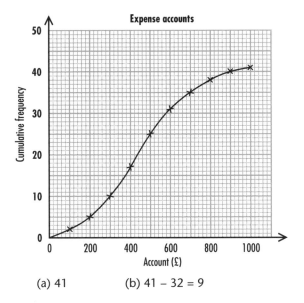

(a) 41   (b) 41 – 32 = 9

6

Weight (kg) Upper limit	Cumulative frequency
48.5	4
49.0	10
49.5	19
50.0	33
50.5	51
51.0	68
51.5	83
52.0	93
52.5	98
53.0	100

5

Length (mm) Upper limit	Cumulative frequency
51	3
52	9
53	23
54	40
55	62
56	78
57	88
58	95
59	99
60	100

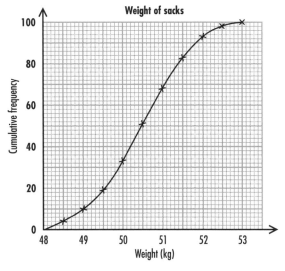

(a) 30   (b) 80th sack weighs 51.8 kg

Exercise 62B

1

Score Upper limit	Cumulative frequency
70	2
80	7
90	14
100	22
110	26
120	28

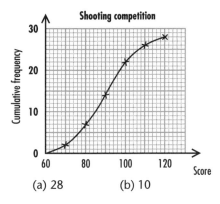

(a) 28   (b) 10

2

Length (mm) Upper limit	Cumulative frequency
25	3
50	9
75	23
100	64
125	84
150	92
175	97
200	100

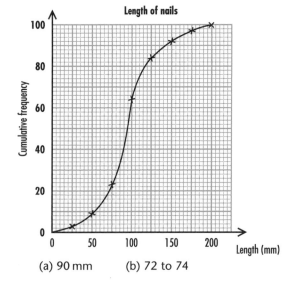

(a) 90 mm   (b) 72 to 74

3

Bill Upper limit	Cumulative frequency
£1	2
£2	6
£3	13
£4	21
£5	32
£6	40
£7	45
£8	47
£9	49
£10	50

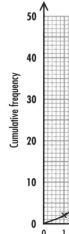

(a) 50   (b) 9 or 10

4

Distance (miles) Upper limit	Cumulative frequency
100	4
200	10
300	19
400	31
500	45
600	55
700	60
800	62

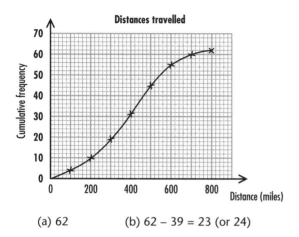

Distances travelled

(a) 62   (b) 62 − 39 = 23 (or 24)

5

Time (s) Upper limit	Cumulative frequency
20	6
40	12
60	25
80	46
100	68
120	82
140	92
160	98
180	100

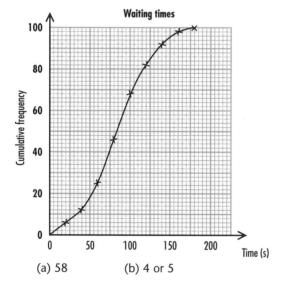

Waiting times

(a) 58   (b) 4 or 5

6

Marks (%) Upper limit	Cumulative frequency
10	2
20	6
30	14
40	28
50	44
60	67
70	79
80	87
90	93
100	95

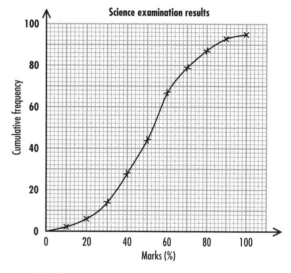

Science examination results

(a) 95
(b) 40% pass and so 60% fail; 60% of 95 is 57 students. Pass mark = 55 or 56%.

63 CUMULATIVE FREQUENCY: MEDIAN AND INTERQUARTILE RANGE

Exercise 63A

1 (a)

Absences (days) Upper limit	Cumulative frequency
5	12
10	27
15	45
20	59
25	73
30	85
35	95
40	103
45	107
50	108

(b)

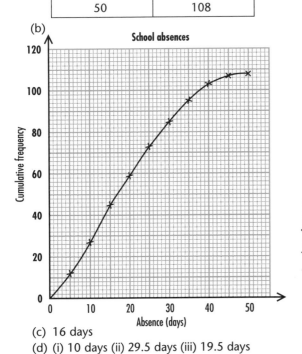

School absences

(c) 16 days

(d) (i) 10 days (ii) 29.5 days (iii) 19.5 days

2 (a)

Marks (%) Upper limit	Cumulative frequency
10	1
20	3
30	8
40	17
50	31
60	45
70	53
80	57
90	59
100	60

(b)

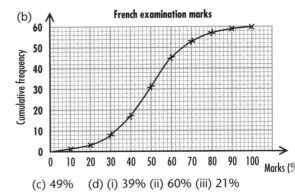

French examination marks

(c) 49%   (d) (i) 39% (ii) 60% (iii) 21%

3 (a)

Time (s) Upper limit	Cumulative frequency
30	11
60	29
90	55
120	97
150	136
180	158
210	175
240	186
270	195
300	200

(b)

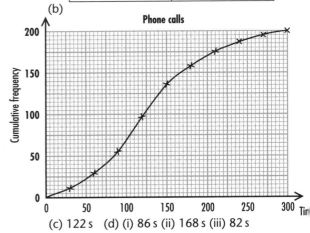

Phone calls

(c) 122 s   (d) (i) 86 s (ii) 168 s (iii) 82 s

4 (a)

Weight (kg) Upper limit	Cumulative frequency
96	1
97	3
98	15
99	32
100	52
101	59
102	65
103	69
104	71
105	72

(b)

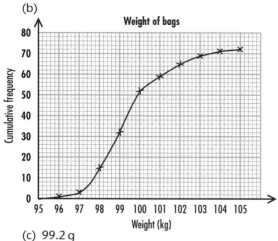

Weight of bags

(c) 99.2 g

(d) (i) 98.2 g (ii) 100.4 g (iii) 2.2 g

5 (a)

Mark (%) Upper limit	Cumulative frequency French	Cumulative frequency German
10	1	0
20	3	2
30	8	7
40	17	16
50	34	26
60	49	37
70	57	48
80	61	57
90	63	61
100	64	64

(b)

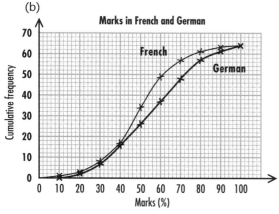

Marks in French and German

(c) French 49%, German 55%

(d) (i) Lower quartile: French 39%
                                    German 40%

    (ii) Upper quartile: French 59%
                                    German 70%

    (iii) IQR: French 20%
                                    German 30%

The median values show that students performed better in German. The IQRs show that the marks in German were more widely spread than in French.

6 (a)

Age (years) Upper limit	Cumulative frequency Egypt	Cumulative frequency Italy
10	19	11
20	36	23
30	51	36
40	63	49
50	73	59
60	78	69
70	82	78
80	86	86
90	88	90
100	88	92

(b)

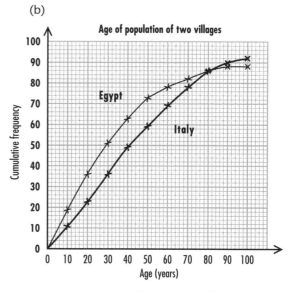

Age of population of two villages

(c) Median: Egypt 25 years, Italy 37 years

(d) (i) Lower quartile: Egypt 12 years
                                    Italy 19 years

    (ii) Upper quartile: Egypt 42 years
                                    Italy 59 years

    (iii) IQR: Egypt 30 years
                                    Italy 40 years

The median values indicate that there are more older people in the Italian village. The IQRs indicates that the population is spread over a wider age range in the Italian village.

Exercise 63B

1 (a)

Height (cm) Upper limit	Cumulative frequency
155	2
160	7
165	20
170	36
175	56
180	70
185	77
190	80

(b)

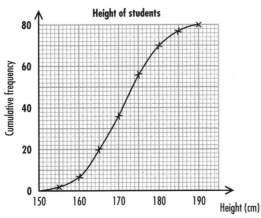

(c) 171 cm

(d)(i) 165 cm (ii) 176 cm (iii) 11 cm

2 (a)

Marks (%) Upper limit	Cumulative frequency
10	0
20	1
30	6
40	14
50	27
60	42
70	53
80	62
90	69
100	72

(b)

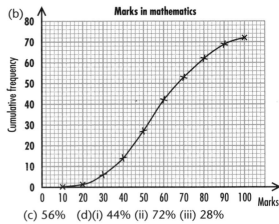

(c) 56% (d)(i) 44% (ii) 72% (iii) 28%

3 (a)

Tip (£) Upper limit	Cumulative frequency
1	2
2	5
3	11
4	19
5	32
6	43
7	50
8	55
9	58
10	60

(b)

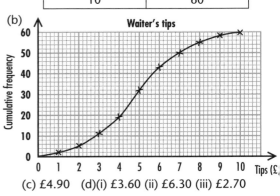

(c) £4.90   (d)(i) £3.60 (ii) £6.30 (iii) £2.70

4 (a)

Pay (× £1000) Upper limit	Cumulative frequency
10	5
12	17
14	33
16	68
18	102
20	127
22	143
24	153
26	157
28	159
30	160

(b)

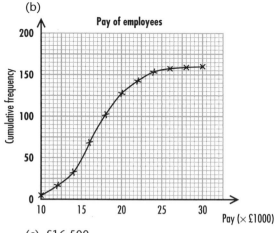

Pay of employees

(c) £16 500

(d) (i) £14 500 (ii) £19 500 (iii) £5000

5 (a)

Time (min) Upper limit	Cumulative frequency (group A)	Cumulative frequency (group B)
12	4	5
14	10	13
16	19	24
18	33	40
20	49	57
22	60	75
24	67	83
26	72	87
28	75	88
30	76	88

(b)

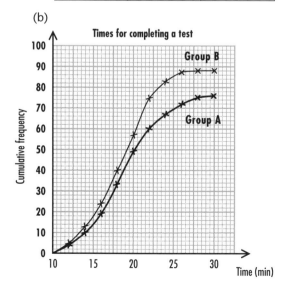

Times for completing a test

(c) Median: A 18.5 min, B 18.5 min
(d) (i) Lower quartile: A 16 min, B 15.7 min
    (ii) Upper quartile: A 21.2 min, B 21 min
    (iii) IQR: A 5.2 min, B 5.3 min

The median and IQR values are very similar for the two groups. The two groups perform very similarly although the sizes of the populations differ.

6 (a)

Age (years) Upper limit	Cumulative frequency UK	Cumulative frequency Philippines
10	28	35
20	58	73
30	90	105
40	118	127
50	141	142
60	160	153
70	178	162
80	190	170
90	198	176
100	200	180

(b)

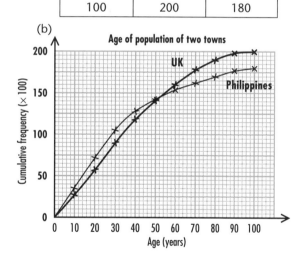

Age of population of two towns

(c) Median: UK 33 years, Philippines 25 years
(d) (i) Lower Quartile: UK 18 years
                        Philippines 12 years
    (ii) Upper Quartile: UK 55 years
                        Philippines 43 years
    (iii) IQR: UK 37 years
              Philippines 31 years

The population in the town in the Philippines is younger and spread over a narrower range of years than the town in the UK.

$\mathcal{R}$ EVISION

Exercise G

1 (a) Mean = $\frac{285}{79}$ = 3.61 people,

mode = 3 people, median = 3 people,
range = 8 – 1 = 7 people

(b) New mean = $\frac{248}{74}$ = 3.35 people,

new range = 6 – 1 = 5 people, mode and median unchanged

2 (a) Untrue – X 31, Y 32

(b) Untrue – One student scored 0 in Class X.

(c) True

(d) Untrue – 5 is the mode for Class X.

3 (a) Tall and thin

(b) Medium height but a little heavier than average for a person of his height

(c) Average height and weight

(d) 73 kg

(e) 150 cm

4 (a)

80	85	90	95 mm
52	97	108	110

(b)

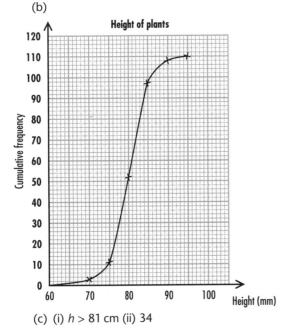

Height of plants

(c) (i) $h > 81$ cm (ii) 34

Exercise GG

1 (a) (i) $\frac{480}{70}$ = 6.9 h (ii) $\frac{496}{70}$ = 7.1 h

(iii) $\frac{496}{70}$ = 7.0 h

(b) A: $8 \leq H < 10$ h, B: $4 \leq H < 6$ h

(c) A and B both $6 \leq H < 8$ h

(d) $8 \leq H < 10$ h

(e) Both! – A has the highest modal class but B has the highest mean.

2 (a) Untrue – Symmetrical about the mark 60%

(b) True

(c) Untrue – There are 2 students in each subject who scored 80–90% but they probably do not add up to the same total.

(d) Untrue – The lines have no significance between the points. So, just because the lines cross, does not mean the marks are the same.

3 (a), (b), (d) and (e)

Cost per board (£)

Cost of boards against number produced

Week 8

Mean values

Week 4

Number of boards per week

(c) 4960, £1.52

(f) (i) 8100 (ii) £1.84–£1.85

4 (a)

Marks (%) Upper limit	Cumulative frequency (maths)	Cumulative frequency (science)
10	2	0
20	5	0
30	10	2
40	17	7
50	25	14
60	36	23
70	48	41
80	57	59
90	62	63
100	64	64

(b)

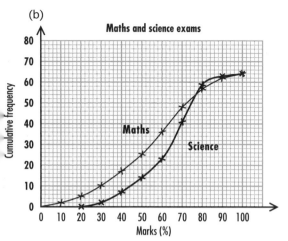

Maths and science exams

(c) Maths 56%, science 65%
(d) Maths (i) 40% (ii) 70% (iii) 30%
   Science (i) 52% (ii) 74% (iii) 22%
(e) The median values indicate that the
   students performed better in the science
   examination. The IQRs indicate that the
   maths results were spread over a wider
   range than the science.

64 PROBABILITY: RELATIVE FREQUENCY USED TO MAKE ESTIMATES

Exercise 64A

1 £84
2 $\frac{220}{500} \times 5 = 2.20\,$kg
3 (a) 97   (b) 350   (c) $\frac{1}{97}$
   (d) No – It is a matter of 'luck' that the results
   are different.
4 (a) 90   (b) $\frac{11}{30}$ (c) 77   (d) $\frac{16}{45}$
5 (a) 100   (b) 0.06 or $\frac{6}{100}$ (c) 0.38 or $\frac{19}{50}$
   (d) win £2.40
6 (a) 14 000
   (b) $\frac{2}{100} \times 56\,000 \approx 1000$
   (c) 10 000 – 8960 = 1040
   (d) Yes – Sue Norris 11 760 + 10 000 = 21 760;
   John Minor 15 120 + 4000 maximum (of
   'Do not know') = 19 120

Exercise 64B

1 $\frac{3}{8}$
2 700
3 (a)(i) 0.06 or $\frac{3}{50}$ (ii) 0.94 or $\frac{47}{50}$ (b) 30p
4 (a) 0.02 or $\frac{1}{50}$ (b) 0.692 or $\frac{173}{250}$ (c) 2
   (d) 12 × 40 = 480

5 (a) 0.16 or $\frac{4}{25}$ (b) 0.02 or $\frac{1}{50}$
  (c) 0.125 or $\frac{1}{8}$ (d) Profit of £1
6 (a) 15%   (b) 20 000   (c) 9000
  (d) Yes – Kate John: 80% of 30 = 24 and so
   $\frac{74}{200} \times 48\,000 \approx 18\,000$

65 PROBABILITY: ADDITION RULE FOR MUTUALLY EXCLUSIVE EVENTS

Exercise 65A

1 (a) $\frac{1}{7}$ (b) $\frac{1}{2}$ (c) $\frac{9}{14}$ (d) $\frac{6}{7}$
2 (a) $\frac{1}{52}$ (b) $\frac{1}{26}$ (c) $\frac{1}{26}$ (d) $\frac{1}{13}$
3 (a) $\frac{1}{2}$ (b) $\frac{1}{2}$ (c) $\frac{2}{3}$ (d) $\frac{1}{2}$
4 (a) $\frac{3}{8}$ (b) $\frac{1}{2}$ (c) $\frac{5}{8}$ (d) $\frac{7}{8}$
5 (a) $\frac{2}{13}$ (b) $\frac{3}{13}$ (c) $\frac{1}{13}$ (d) $\frac{4}{13}$
6 (a) $\frac{1}{7}$ (b) $\frac{5}{7}$ (c) $\frac{3}{7}$ (d) $\frac{6}{7}$
7 (a) $\frac{4}{13}$ (b) $\frac{9}{13}$ (c) $\frac{6}{13}$ (d) $\frac{12}{13}$
8 (a) 0.125   (b) 0.3125   (c) 0.3125
  (d) 0.625
9 (a) (i) $\frac{1}{12}$ (ii) $\frac{1}{3}$ (iii) $\frac{11}{36}$ (iv) $\frac{1}{6}$
  (b) (i) $\frac{1}{2}$ (ii) $\frac{1}{2}$ – the same
10 (a) (i) $\frac{1}{3}$ (ii) $\frac{1}{5}$ (iii) $\frac{1}{3}$ (iv) $\frac{1}{2}$
  (b)(i) $\frac{1}{2}$ (ii) $\frac{1}{2}$ – same

Exercise 65B

1 (a) $\frac{2}{5}$ (b) $\frac{17}{25}$ (c) $\frac{18}{25}$ (d) $\frac{3}{5}$
2 (a) $\frac{1}{2}$ (b) $\frac{1}{2}$ (c) $\frac{1}{4}$ (d) $\frac{3}{8}$
3 (a) $\frac{1}{26}$ (b) $\frac{1}{52}$ (c) $\frac{1}{13}$ (d) $\frac{3}{13}$
4 (a) $\frac{1}{3}$ (b) $\frac{2}{3}$ (c) $\frac{2}{3}$ (d) $\frac{8}{15}$
5 (a) $\frac{1}{4}$ (b) $\frac{5}{16}$ (c) $\frac{11}{16}$ (d) $\frac{11}{16}$
6 (a) $\frac{1}{52}$ (b) $\frac{1}{26}$ (c) $\frac{1}{26}$ (d) $\frac{1}{13}$
7 (a) $\frac{1}{5}$ (b) $\frac{4}{5}$ (c) $\frac{7}{10}$ (d) $\frac{1}{2}$
8 (a) $\frac{1}{4}$ (b) $\frac{1}{2}$ (c) $\frac{7}{8}$ (d) $\frac{3}{4}$
9 (a) (i) 0.24 (ii) 0.36 (iii) 0.36 (iv) 0.12
  (b) (i) 0.52 (ii) 0.48 – even score
10 (a) $\frac{1}{16}$ (b) $\frac{1}{2}$ (c) $\frac{1}{2}$ (d) $\frac{15}{32}$

66 PROBABILITY: MULTIPLICATION RULE FOR TWO INDEPENDENT EVENTS

Exercise 66A

1 (a) $\frac{1}{36}$ (b) $\frac{1}{4}$ (c) $\frac{1}{4}$ (d) $\frac{1}{12}$

2 (a) $\frac{1}{9}$ or 0.11   (b) $\frac{4}{9}$ or 0.44

   (c) $\frac{2}{9}$ or 0.22   (d) $\frac{2}{9}$ or 0.22

3 (a) $\frac{1}{25}$ or 0.04   (b) $\frac{9}{25}$ or 0.36

   (c) $\frac{4}{25}$ or 0.16   (d) $\frac{1}{25}$ or 0.04

4 (a) $\frac{1}{78}$ or 0.0128   (b) $\frac{1}{104}$ or 0.009 62

   (c) $\frac{1}{26}$ or 0.0384   (d) $\frac{2}{13}$ or 0.154

5 (a) $\frac{13}{102}$ or 0.128   (b) $\frac{13}{204}$ or 0.0637

   (c) $\frac{25}{102}$ or 0.245   (d) $\frac{1}{17}$ or 0.0588

6 (a) $\frac{9}{10}$ (b) 0   (c) $\frac{1}{20}$ (d) $\frac{1}{20}$

7 (a) $\frac{1}{36}$ (b) $\frac{1}{4}$ (c) $\frac{1}{36}$ (d) $\frac{1}{18}$

8 (a) $\frac{1}{17}$ or 0.0588   (b) $\frac{25}{102}$ or 0.245

   (c) $\frac{1}{221}$ or 0.004 52   (d) $\frac{4}{663}$ or 0.005 603

9 (a) 0.3   (b) 0.2   (c) 0.3   (d) 0.5

10 (a) $\frac{25}{64}$ or 0.391   (b) $\frac{1}{64}$ or 0.0156

   (c) $\frac{5}{32}$ or 0.156

   (d) $1 - \frac{25}{64} - \frac{1}{16} = \frac{35}{64}$ or 0.547

Exercise 66B

1 (a) $\frac{6}{25}$ or 0.24   (b) $\frac{9}{25}$ or 0.36

   (c) $\frac{4}{25}$ or 0.16   (d) $\frac{13}{25}$ or 0.52

2 (a) $\frac{1}{36}$ (b) $\frac{1}{9}$ (c) $\frac{1}{18}$ (d) $\frac{1}{9}$

3 (a) $\frac{4}{25}$ (b) $\frac{9}{25}$ (c) $\frac{6}{25}$ (d) $\frac{12}{25}$

4 (a) $\frac{1}{36}$ or 0.0278   (b) $\frac{1}{36}$ or 0.0278

   (c) $\frac{1}{36}$ or 0.0278   (d) $\frac{1}{6}$ or 0.167

5 (a) $\frac{1}{17}$ or 0.0588   (b) $\frac{13}{51}$ or 0.255

   (c) $\frac{13}{51}$ or 0.255   (d) $\frac{26}{51}$ or 0.510

6 (a) $\frac{1}{2}$ (b) $\frac{1}{12}$ (c) $\frac{1}{6}$

   (d) $\frac{1}{6} + \frac{1}{4} = \frac{5}{12}$ or 0.417

7 (a) $\frac{1}{11}$ or 0.0909   (b) $\frac{5}{33}$ or 0.152

   (c) $\frac{5}{44}$ or 0.114   (d) $\frac{5}{22}$ or 0.227

8 (a) $\frac{4}{663}$ or 0.006 03   (b) $\frac{1}{221}$ or 0.004 52

   (c) $\frac{1}{17}$ or 0.0588   (d) $\frac{11}{221}$ or 0.0498

9 (a) 0.09   (b) 0.01   (c) 0.36

   (d) $1 - 0.36 - 0.01 = 0.63$

10 (a) $\frac{1}{16}$ or 0.0625   (b) $\frac{1}{16}$ or 0.0625

   (c) $\frac{1}{256}$ or 0.00391   (d) $\frac{1}{8} + \frac{1}{8} = \frac{1}{4}$ or 0.25

67 PROBABILITY: TREE DIAGRAMS

Exercise 67A

1 (a)

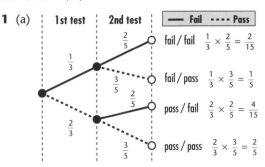

(b) (i) $\frac{2}{15}$ (ii) $\frac{2}{5}$ (iii) $\frac{3}{15} + \frac{4}{15} = \frac{7}{15}$

2 (a)

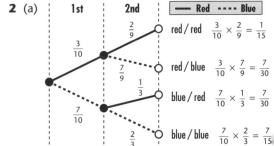

(b) (i) $\frac{1}{15}$ or 0.0667 (ii) $\frac{7}{15}$ or 0.467

     (iii) $\frac{7}{15}$ or 0.467

3 (a)

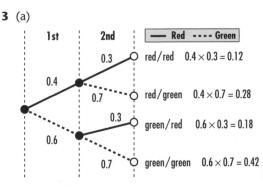

(b) (i) 0.12 (ii) 0.42 (iii) 0.42 + 0.12 = 0.54

     (iv) 0.18 + 0.28 = 0.46

4 (a)

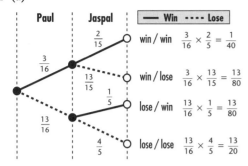

Paul   Jaspal   [— Win ···· Lose]

$\frac{2}{15}$ win / win $\frac{3}{16} \times \frac{2}{5} = \frac{1}{40}$

$\frac{3}{16}$ $\frac{13}{15}$ win / lose $\frac{3}{16} \times \frac{13}{15} = \frac{13}{80}$

$\frac{1}{5}$ lose / win $\frac{13}{16} \times \frac{1}{5} = \frac{13}{80}$

$\frac{13}{16}$ $\frac{4}{5}$ lose / lose $\frac{13}{16} \times \frac{4}{5} = \frac{13}{20}$

(b) (i) $\frac{13}{80}$ or 0.1625 (ii) $\frac{13}{80}$ or 0.1625

(iii) $\frac{1}{40}$ or 0.0250 (iv) $\frac{13}{20}$ or 0.65

5 (a)

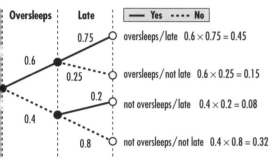

Oversleeps   Late   [— Yes ···· No]

0.75 oversleeps / late $0.6 \times 0.75 = 0.45$

0.6   0.25 oversleeps / not late $0.6 \times 0.25 = 0.15$

0.2 not oversleeps / late $0.4 \times 0.2 = 0.08$

0.4   0.8 not oversleeps / not late $0.4 \times 0.8 = 0.32$

(b) (i) 0.08 (ii) 0.15 (iii) 0.45 + 0.08 = 0.53
(iv) 0.15 + 0.32 = 0.47

6 (a)

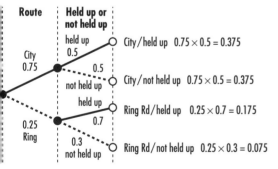

Route   Held up or not held up

held up 0.5   City / held up $0.75 \times 0.5 = 0.375$

City 0.75   0.5 not held up   City / not held up $0.75 \times 0.5 = 0.375$

held up 0.7   Ring Rd / held up $0.25 \times 0.7 = 0.175$

0.25 Ring   0.3 not held up   Ring Rd / not held up $0.25 \times 0.3 = 0.075$

(b) (i) 0.175 (ii) 0.375
(iii) 0.175 + 0.375 = 0.55
(iv) 0.075 + 0.375 = 0.45

7 (a)

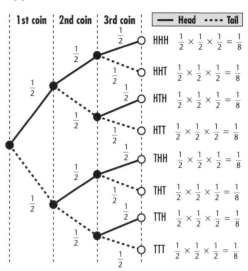

1st coin   2nd coin   3rd coin   [— Head ···· Tail]

$\frac{1}{2}$ HHH $\frac{1}{2} \times \frac{1}{2} \times \frac{1}{2} = \frac{1}{8}$

HHT $\frac{1}{2} \times \frac{1}{2} \times \frac{1}{2} = \frac{1}{8}$

HTH $\frac{1}{2} \times \frac{1}{2} \times \frac{1}{2} = \frac{1}{8}$

HTT $\frac{1}{2} \times \frac{1}{2} \times \frac{1}{2} = \frac{1}{8}$

THH $\frac{1}{2} \times \frac{1}{2} \times \frac{1}{2} = \frac{1}{8}$

THT $\frac{1}{2} \times \frac{1}{2} \times \frac{1}{2} = \frac{1}{8}$

TTH $\frac{1}{2} \times \frac{1}{2} \times \frac{1}{2} = \frac{1}{8}$

TTT $\frac{1}{2} \times \frac{1}{2} \times \frac{1}{2} = \frac{1}{8}$

(b) (i) $\frac{1}{8}$ (ii) $\frac{1}{8}$ (iii) $\frac{1}{8} + \frac{1}{8} = \frac{1}{4}$ (iv) $\frac{6}{8} = \frac{3}{4}$

8 (a)

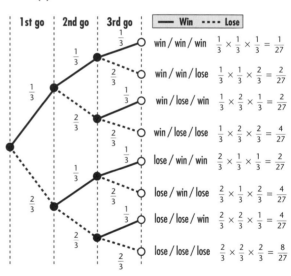

1st go   2nd go   3rd go   [— Win ···· Lose]

$\frac{1}{3}$ win / win / win $\frac{1}{3} \times \frac{1}{3} \times \frac{1}{3} = \frac{1}{27}$

$\frac{1}{3}$ $\frac{2}{3}$ win / win / lose $\frac{1}{3} \times \frac{1}{3} \times \frac{2}{3} = \frac{2}{27}$

$\frac{1}{3}$ win / lose / win $\frac{1}{3} \times \frac{2}{3} \times \frac{1}{3} = \frac{2}{27}$

$\frac{2}{3}$ $\frac{2}{3}$ win / lose / lose $\frac{1}{3} \times \frac{2}{3} \times \frac{2}{3} = \frac{4}{27}$

$\frac{1}{3}$ lose / win / win $\frac{2}{3} \times \frac{1}{3} \times \frac{1}{3} = \frac{2}{27}$

$\frac{1}{3}$ $\frac{2}{3}$ lose / win / lose $\frac{2}{3} \times \frac{1}{3} \times \frac{2}{3} = \frac{4}{27}$

$\frac{2}{3}$ $\frac{1}{3}$ lose / lose / win $\frac{2}{3} \times \frac{2}{3} \times \frac{1}{3} = \frac{4}{27}$

$\frac{2}{3}$ $\frac{2}{3}$ lose / lose / lose $\frac{2}{3} \times \frac{2}{3} \times \frac{2}{3} = \frac{8}{27}$

(b) (i) £50: $\frac{1}{27}$, £1: $\frac{2}{27} \times 3 = \frac{2}{9}$,

10p: $\frac{4}{27} \times 3 = \frac{4}{9}$

(c) $\frac{8}{27}$

9 (a)

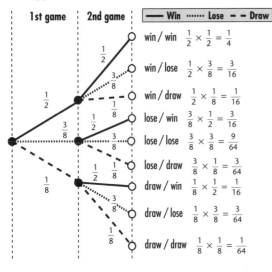

1st game | 2nd game | —— Win ······· Lose – – Draw

win / win $\frac{1}{2} \times \frac{1}{2} = \frac{1}{4}$

win / lose $\frac{1}{2} \times \frac{3}{8} = \frac{3}{16}$

win / draw $\frac{1}{2} \times \frac{1}{8} = \frac{1}{16}$

lose / win $\frac{3}{8} \times \frac{1}{2} = \frac{3}{16}$

lose / lose $\frac{3}{8} \times \frac{3}{8} = \frac{9}{64}$

lose / draw $\frac{3}{8} \times \frac{1}{8} = \frac{3}{64}$

draw / win $\frac{1}{8} \times \frac{1}{2} = \frac{1}{16}$

draw / lose $\frac{1}{8} \times \frac{3}{8} = \frac{3}{64}$

draw / draw $\frac{1}{8} \times \frac{1}{8} = \frac{1}{64}$

(b) (i) $\frac{1}{4}$ (ii) $\frac{1}{64}$ (iii) $\frac{9}{64}$

(iv) $\frac{3}{16} + \frac{1}{16} + \frac{3}{16} + \frac{1}{16} = \frac{1}{2}$

10 (a)

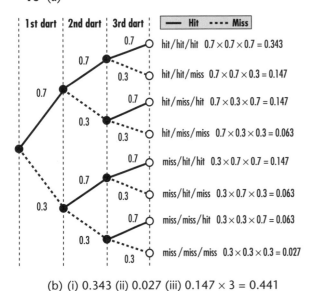

1st dart | 2nd dart | 3rd dart | —— Hit ···· Miss

hit/hit/hit $0.7 \times 0.7 \times 0.7 = 0.343$

hit/hit/miss $0.7 \times 0.7 \times 0.3 = 0.147$

hit/miss/hit $0.7 \times 0.3 \times 0.7 = 0.147$

hit/miss/miss $0.7 \times 0.3 \times 0.3 = 0.063$

miss/hit/hit $0.3 \times 0.7 \times 0.7 = 0.147$

miss/hit/miss $0.3 \times 0.7 \times 0.3 = 0.063$

miss/miss/hit $0.3 \times 0.3 \times 0.7 = 0.063$

miss/miss/miss $0.3 \times 0.3 \times 0.3 = 0.027$

(b) (i) 0.343 (ii) 0.027 (iii) $0.147 \times 3 = 0.441$
(iv) $0.063 \times 3 = 0.189$

Exercise 67B

1 (a)

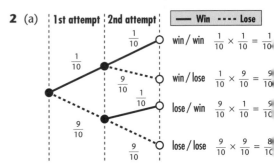

100 m | 200 m | —— Win ···· Lose

win / win $\frac{2}{3} \times \frac{3}{4} = \frac{1}{2}$

win / lose $\frac{2}{3} \times \frac{1}{4} = \frac{1}{6}$

lose / win $\frac{1}{3} \times \frac{3}{4} = \frac{1}{4}$

lose / lose $\frac{1}{3} \times \frac{1}{4} = \frac{1}{12}$

(b) (i) $\frac{1}{2}$ (ii) $\frac{1}{12}$ (iii) $\frac{1}{6} + \frac{1}{4} = \frac{5}{12}$

2 (a)

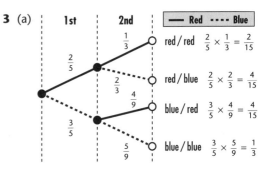

1st attempt | 2nd attempt | —— Win ···· Lose

win / win $\frac{1}{10} \times \frac{1}{10} = \frac{1}{100}$

win / lose $\frac{1}{10} \times \frac{9}{10} = \frac{9}{100}$

lose / win $\frac{9}{10} \times \frac{1}{10} = \frac{9}{100}$

lose / lose $\frac{9}{10} \times \frac{9}{10} = \frac{81}{100}$

(b) (i) $\frac{1}{100}$ (ii) $\frac{9}{100} + \frac{9}{100} = \frac{9}{50}$ (iii) $\frac{81}{100}$

3 (a)

1st | 2nd | —— Red ···· Blue

red / red $\frac{2}{5} \times \frac{1}{3} = \frac{2}{15}$

red / blue $\frac{2}{5} \times \frac{2}{3} = \frac{4}{15}$

blue / red $\frac{3}{5} \times \frac{4}{9} = \frac{4}{15}$

blue / blue $\frac{3}{5} \times \frac{5}{9} = \frac{1}{3}$

(b) (i) $\frac{2}{15}$ or 0.133 (ii) $\frac{1}{3}$ or 0.333

(iii) $\frac{8}{15}$ or 0.533

4 (a)

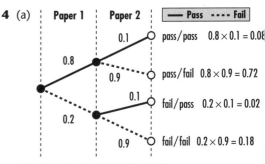

Paper 1 | Paper 2 | —— Pass ···· Fail

pass/pass $0.8 \times 0.1 = 0.08$

pass/fail $0.8 \times 0.9 = 0.72$

fail/pass $0.2 \times 0.1 = 0.02$

fail/fail $0.2 \times 0.9 = 0.18$

(b) (i) 0.72 (ii) 0.08 (iii) 0.18
(iv) $0.72 + 0.02 = 0.74$

5 (a) (i) $\frac{1}{2}$ (ii) $\frac{1}{3}$

(b)

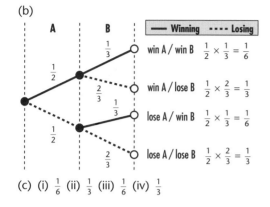

(c) (i) $\frac{1}{6}$ (ii) $\frac{1}{3}$ (iii) $\frac{1}{6}$ (iv) $\frac{1}{3}$

6 (a)

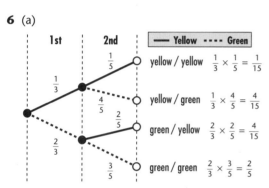

(b) (i) $\frac{2}{5}$ (ii) $\frac{1}{15}$ or 0.0667 (iii) $\frac{8}{15}$ or 0.533

7 (a)

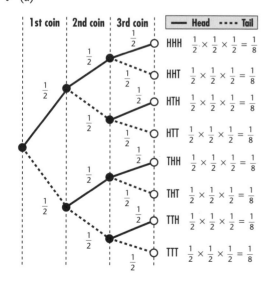

(b) (i) $\frac{1}{8}$ (ii) $\frac{1}{8}$ (iii) $\frac{3}{8}$ (iv) $\frac{1}{2}$

8 (a)

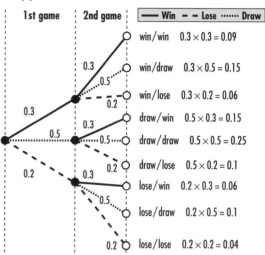

(b) (i) 0.09 (ii) 0.04 (iii) 0.25
(iv) $0.15 + 0.15 + 0.06 + 0.06 = 0.42$

9 (a) $\frac{3}{8}$ (b) $\frac{1}{3}$

(c)

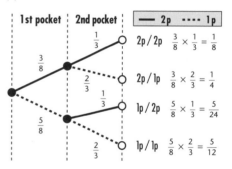

(d) (i) $\frac{1}{8}$ (ii) $\frac{5}{12}$ (iii) $\frac{1}{4} + \frac{5}{24} = \frac{11}{24}$ or 0.458
(iv) $\frac{11}{24} + \frac{1}{8} = \frac{7}{12}$ or 0.292

10 (a)

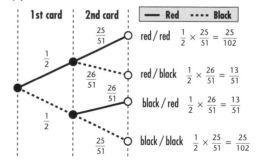

(b) (i) $\frac{25}{102}$ or 0.245 (ii) $\frac{25}{102}$ or 0.245
(iii) $\frac{26}{51}$ or 0.510 (iv) $\frac{77}{102}$ or 0.755

Exercise ††

1 £58.00

2 896

3 (a) $\frac{3}{20}$ (b) $\frac{9}{20}$ (c) $\frac{7}{10}$ (d) $\frac{17}{20}$

4 (a) $\frac{1}{52}$ (b) $\frac{1}{26}$ (c) $\frac{1}{26}$ (d) $\frac{1}{13}$

5 $\frac{1}{26}$

6 0.81

7 (a)

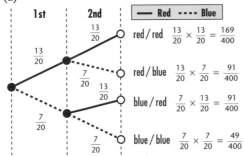

    (b) (i) $\frac{169}{400}$ or 0.4225 (ii) $\frac{49}{400}$ or 0.1225

       (iii) $\frac{182}{400}$ or 0.455

Exercise †††

1 (a) $\frac{7}{15}$ or 0.467   (b) $\frac{7}{26}$ or 0.269

  (c) $\frac{5}{12}$ or 0.417   (d) 560

2 (a) (i) 0.4 (ii) 0.35 (iii) 0.3 (iv) 0.3

  (b) (i) 0.5 (ii) 0.5 – same

3 (a) $\frac{1}{16}$ (b) $\frac{9}{16}$ (c) $\frac{3}{16}$ (d) $\frac{3}{16}$

4 (a)

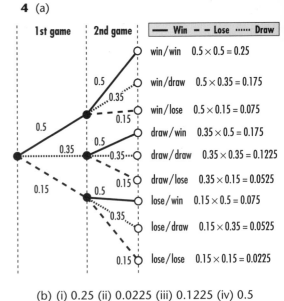

    (b) (i) 0.25 (ii) 0.0225 (iii) 0.1225 (iv) 0.5